DBT - Skills Workbook
for
Borderline Personality Disorder

145 Highly Effective Activities

How to Control Your Intense Emotions, Reduce Your Self-Destructive Behaviors, and Improve Your Relationships

By

Christopher B. K. Edward & Nazish Idrees, PhD

Acknowledgement

Co-Authors:

Jeffry K. Kornstedt, PhD, Dialectical Behavioral Therapist

Naziah Idrees, PhD, Dialectical Behavioral Therapist

Jessica L. Oglethorpe, PhD, Dialectical Behavioral Therapist

© Copyright 2022 - All rights reserved.

The content contained within this book may not be reproduced, duplicated or transmitted without direct written permission from the author or the publisher.

Under no circumstances will any blame or legal responsibility be held against the publisher, or author, for any damages, reparation, or monetary loss due to the information contained within this book, either directly or indirectly.

Legal Notice:

This book is copyright protected. It is only for personal use. You cannot amend, distribute, sell, use, quote or paraphrase any part, or the content within this book, without the consent of the author or publisher.

Disclaimer Notice:

Please note the information contained within this document is for educational and entertainment purposes only. All effort has been executed to present accurate, up to date, reliable, complete information. No warranties of any kind are declared or implied. Readers acknowledge that the author is not engaged in the rendering of legal, financial, medical or professional advice. The content within this book has been derived from various sources. Please consult a licensed professional before attempting any techniques outlined in this book.

By reading this document, the reader agrees that under no circumstances is the author responsible for any losses, direct or indirect, that are incurred as a result of the use of the information contained within this document, including, but not limited to, errors, omissions, or inaccuracies.

GIFT FOR YOU!

Top 5 Distress Tolerance Skills

Habits for tolerating painful events, urges, and emotions when you cannot make things better immediately.

You can download this free guide from the link below:

https://dbtorcbt.com/

Contents

Introduction

A re you desperate to feel "normal?" To simply fit in and get on with your life?

Would you like to get rid of the inner demons and stop the constant mood changes and the battles you fight within yourself to stay in control and feel normal?

- 1.6% of the general population worldwide is dealing with BPD

- among 20% of in-patients receiving psychiatric care are diagnosed with BPD (Chapman et al.)

No one completely understands borderline personality disorder (BPD), not even you. It is a very real syndrome and you know how much it can confuse and hurt—you and everyone else connected to your life.

We know you feel intense anger at your lack of self-control, the emotional outbursts that are always beyond your control, and the sleepless nights you spend worrying over all the hurt you may have caused to those you love and yourself.

What we are offering you here is a solution that is beyond therapy or counseling and trying to talk your way toward a solution. Contained in this book are simple activities that will help you overcome your challenges. Actions speak louder than words, and that is exactly what we want you to start experiencing.

We can help you overcome your condition because we are a part of a community made up of people who have been in your situation.

Helping Hand is a small organization made up of people who have endured very similar experiences between themselves because of BPD. Their experiences are varied as they have dealt with BPD on different levels, having been exposed to the condition themselves, through family members, or having a partner diagnosed with BPD. Because of this exposure, and by striving to analyze and understand the condition on a personal level, we can offer you several solutions born from a combined effort of activities and coping strategies that have been effectively tested and proven to work for many desperate to get their lives under control.

Understanding Borderline Personality Disorder (BPD)

BPD is not an easy-to-understand condition. It affects your thoughts about yourself and others. There is nothing harder to fathom than a suspicious and wandering mind that can't settle on a decision.

The main characteristics of BPD:

- Feelings of insecurity and unstable emotions can be intense and overwhelming.

- You will experience bouts of self-doubt.

- Fluctuating moods.

- Sudden anger.

- Unstable thoughts and behavior that sabotage relationships.

- You will suffer from low self-esteem and constant nervousness.

- Paranoia will set in when you are most distressed.

- You fear abandonment as well as instability in your life.

- Feelings of emptiness.

BPD is never experienced alone. Quite often, the condition is coupled with other disorders.

- eating disorders

- anxiety syndromes

- depression

- substance abuse

- bipolar disorder

- post-traumatic stress disorder (PTSD)

Can I Have BPD—What Are the Signs?

A person dealing with BPD will struggle to manage their thoughts, emotions, and behavior. Self-regulation is tough, and they are constantly dealing with low self-esteem and maintaining their relationships. Someone who exhibits five of the personality traits associated with BPD will be diagnosed as dealing with BPD; likewise, those personality traits should interfere with their lifestyles.

Symptoms of BPD no one talks about

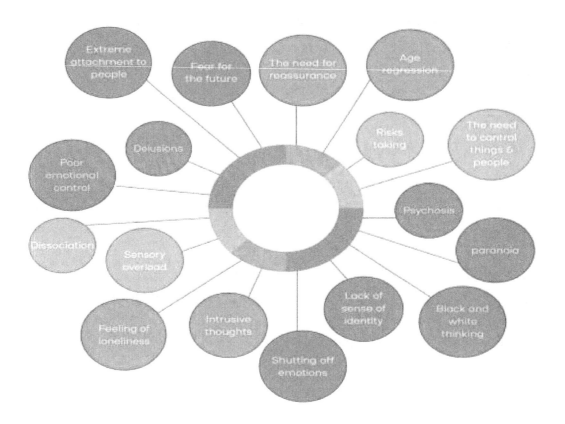

Identified traits of borderline personality disorder:

- A cycle of broken relationships. People with BPD have a string of unstable relationships. Devaluations, hurt, and volatile anger are a part of the insecurity felt by someone in a relationship dealing with BPD.

- Explosive temper is a common trait in people dealing with BPD. They have little or no control over their tempers and will be quick to react with extreme rage. Once this rage rears its head, it will manifest in different ways. Someone with BPD will not always express their extreme rage through an emotional outburst; instead, they will let it fester inside and resort to extremes like self-harm.

- Engaging in self-harming actions. Indulging in risky behavior makes the person dealing with a challenging emotion resort to self-harm as a type of distraction. Suicidal thoughts are common, as are actions that cause harm.

  ○ Cutting oneself or engaging in any other self-harming infliction.

  ○ Knowing the risks and binge drinking.

  ○ Engaging in unsafe sexual encounters.

  ○ Addiction to recreational drugs.

Death may not be the intention when this type of self-harm is initiated; it's often a type of distraction that is used to numb the pain of something the person does not wish to face—it is a form of emotional regulation.

- Entertaining thoughts of worthlessness. People with BPD often deal with a feeling of inadequacy; they feel empty, as though something inside of them is missing. Destructive habits like drugs, alcoholism, and risky sexual encounters are sought out as replacements to fill the void.

- Disassociation and suspicion. Losing touch with reality is another trait associated with BPD. Such people deal with constant suspicion of people, overanalyzing what they say and do. At times, their thoughts will become foggy, and they will feel apart from their body, unable to feel or connect with reality.

What Is DBT?

Dialectical behavior therapy is a form of psychotherapy—a type of talk therapy that helps people to overcome their destructive behavior and interactions to lead more satisfied and happier lives.

DBT is given the gold standard in treatment as one of the most successful types of treatment against BPD, focusing on improving cognitive skills by helping you change your thoughts, beliefs, and behavior. It improves emotional regulation and offers better control of actions.

Derived from traditional cognitive behavior therapy (CBT), DBT includes a few changes to the methods of how the treatment is conducted. The success of DBT lies in its key focus: the therapy aims at addressing the core trigger of borderline personality disorder, which is emotional dysregulation.

Documented success has proved the effectiveness of DBT against BPD (Guillén Botella et al.). There are significant reductions in self-inflictive behavior, suicidal thoughts and behavior, substance abuse, and lowered psychiatric treatment and hospital stays recorded among people diagnosed with BPD.

Included in this book are exercises based on DBT skills designed to overcome the fear of abandonment and the destructive behavior that follows.

- Skills to manage interpersonal effectiveness—learn to manage your relationships by taking control of your behavior and emotions when dealing with conflicts. Stop overreacting and then regretting your actions.

- Increase your distress tolerance levels—learn to take control and improve your emotional regulation so you don't overreact and engage in self-harmful behavior. It's normal for someone dealing with BPD to view self-infliction as a means of escape. It's an outlet that distracts them from the issue they want to avoid. Sadly, it often leads to serious self-harm. By learning to tolerate distress better, you will gain more control over your emotions before they take charge of your behavior.

- Emotional regulation—learn to manage and express your emotions less reactively. Taking control of your emotions will help you to better manage your responses rather than reacting in anger or sudden distress. Emotional regulation is about.

- Mindfulness meditation—this invaluable tool will help teach you to be in the present by being a part of what's happening around you. Mindfulness will teach you to be in the "now." Be a part of what's happening and become observant of your environment. It's important to stop your wandering mind and to overanalyze situations, comments, and behavior; a bad trait of BPD that leads to anger and overreacting, which is a highly disruptive and destructive way to think. Through mindfulness meditation, you learn to become immersed in what's happening at that moment instead of dwelling on thoughts long enough to analyze them and form toxic opinions that end up harming you.

Each chapter contains exercises to help you overcome the setbacks brought on by your borderline personality disorder. The exercises are carefully compiled and presented in simple, easy-to-understand steps, guaranteeing maximum success—you will not feel overwhelmed or confused; instead, for the first time, you are going to see a ray of light shining through all the confusion that has clouded your mind as you begin to experience a positive change in your behavior.

Chapter ONE

The Overwhelming Fear of Abandonment That Comes With BPD

When I tried to imagine being beautiful, I could only imagine living without the perpetual fear of being alone, without the great burden of isolation, which is what feeling ugly felt like

– Lucy Grealy

Have you sabotaged your relationships too many times and pushed people out of your life by allowing suspicion to rule so much that now your biggest fear is being alone?

That is what BPD does—it pushes you to overreact emotionally and physically to the brink of abandonment. This constant self-sabotage brings bout the fear of being alone for the rest of your life—yet you can't stop your disruptive behavior.

In this chapter, we are going to help you overcome the fear of abandonment by teaching you to stop your disruptive behavior. You will be armed with simple skills to help you overcome the fear of rejection and desertion, but first, let's explore the root cause of your anxiety—you must be able to identify the incidents that led to you acquiring this emotional turmoil to begin the healing process and conquer your emotions and behavior.

It's a Tough Trek Uphill, But You Can Make It—Changing Your Perceptions

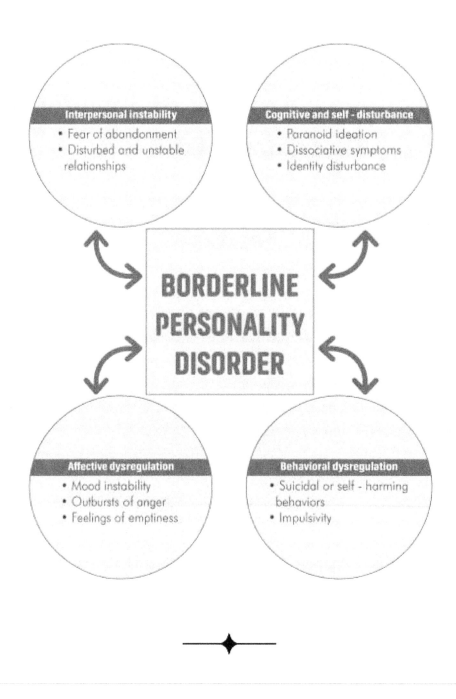

Understanding the Fear of Abandonment

Your relationship status may be in a constant loop; you meet someone, constantly agonize and visualize abandonment, and react negatively. What you perceive to be a failsafe mechanism is, in reality, a self-sabotaging reaction you can't help repeating.

- Impulsive nature and reactions to problems.

- Anger that is out of place.

- Oversharing and becoming too dependent.

- Being quick to lash out at those you love.

- Making the partner feel worthless by devaluing them.

The above slew of reactions from a person dealing with BPD leads to a dysfunctional relationship dynamic.

Cora and James, the Perfectly Imperfect Couple

James was handsome, smart, and well-connected. He would often visit the local pub for a drink with his friends on a Friday. He bumped into Cora one day and was immediately struck by her shy smile and pretty face.

From the moment she bumped into James that first day, Cora was attracted to him and hoped she would see him again, although she told herself he was too good-looking and seemed to be popular which were both black marks against him dating someone like her. You see, Cora was dealing with BPD, which gave her very low self-esteem, and she never saw how pretty she was. When James initiated a relationship, she was both cautious and delighted but was too attracted to him to deny his request.

Three months into the relationship, Cora started suspecting James of flirting with other women. She would spend some nights in tears thinking he was having an affair, all because she felt she was not good enough for him and was waiting for the inevitable rejection she thought was going to follow. Her insecurity caused several rifts between the pair; if James impulsively bought her flowers, she suspected he was apologizing for cheating on her. Or if he introduced her to an attractive female colleague, she would wallow in self-pity, thinking of James being around attractive women while being stuck with her as a girlfriend.

Despite how much he loved and adored her, James found the relationship very tiring and hard to maintain. He spent a lot of time reassuring Cora's insecurities and found her clingy nature hard to handle. He inevitably ended up putting on an act in front of her, preventing him from being the fun-loving, carefree person he was. Through it all, Cora sensing his change, kept expecting the break-up when James finally saw her for who she was, a failure and not good-looking enough for him—her low self-esteem prevented her from realizing that it was she who was pushing their relationship to the edge of the cliff. In reality, James wanted to marry her, but he was confused at how much the Cora he first met had changed. The catalyst came when James was asked to attend an overseas conference with his colleagues; Cora insisted he break up before leaving as she wanted to avoid the humiliation of him having an affair with his attractive female colleague while overseas. James agreed, confused and sad.

What could Cora do to prevent this cycle from repeating over and over?

Stop the Fear of Abandonment

There is hope through all your inner fears and dread of abandonment. The next set of exercises will help you to understand and take control of your emotions, thoughts, and behavior through three aspects of learning.

- Being mindful of the fear of abandonment.

- Learning about distress tolerance.

- Developing interpersonal effectiveness.

1. Being Mindful About the Fear of Abandonment

We all experience abandonment at some point; it is traumatic and can affect each one of us on a different level. Abandonment activates negative emotions, changing our perspective of ourselves and the environment around us. If you feel scared of abandonment, and it's affecting your interactions with others, then the following exercise will help you evaluate and come to terms with your situation, your mind's perception of the hurt, and finally, acceptance, which initiates the healing process.

Exercise 1: For Dealing With Fear of Abandonment—Self Evaluation

Name the person who abandoned you:	Rate your answers on a scale of 1–10
What level of intimacy was shared in the relationship, and how close were you?	(1 not much—10 very close)
How hurt were you when the relationship ended?	(1 not at all—10 very hurt)
How confused were you when the relationship ended?	(1 not bothered—10 very confused)
How insecure did the abandonment make you feel?	(1 not at all—10 extremely self-doubtful)
How did abandonment affect your relationships with other people?	(1 not at all—10 I became very suspicious and mistrustful)
How trustful were you before this relationship ended?	(1 I had no trust issues—10 I had trust issues)
How powerless did you feel after the abandonment?	(1 not at all—10 deflated and beaten)
Do you now have commitment issues?	(1 not at all—10 quite a lot)
Have you been able to forgive this person?	(1 yes—10 not at all)
Do you see yourself doing the same to someone else?	(1 not at all—10 probably)

Run through your answers, evaluate each one and ask yourself how much you have changed because of the abandonment. Do you like the person you have become? For example, if you enjoyed friendships and socializing, how much have you changed since the relationship ended? Do you doubt your self-worth and how attractive you are as a person?

- Know that these evaluations of yourself are not true since you are seeing yourself through the eyes of abandonment.

- Become mindful of the relationship's effect on you in terms of your personality and self-worth becoming underrated. Don't dwell on the damage and make a resolution to put a stop to derogatory thoughts and introverted actions.

- Go back and reevaluate the scores thinking from a perspective before the abandonment took place—is there a change in your values and trust issues?

- Push yourself to overcome the vulnerabilities you are facing.

Exercise 2: Practice Affirmations to Rebuild Your Self-Esteem

What Are Affirmations?

Positive statements that help remind you of your self-worth are affirmations. They increase your sense of worth and work like self-help therapy.

The practice works by manifesting positive images and thoughts of yourself through the repetition of constructive sentences because it can change your perception of your self-esteem through simple constructive and uplifting statements repeated daily.

You can replace a negative thought by introducing a positive one to override it. This happens because your brain is capable of changing and adapting to certain situations when coaxed. This is called neuroplasticity.

Affirmation Worksheet

- Dedicate five minutes a day to repeating affirmations.

- Choose three affirmations that you feel connected to.

- Repeat each affirmation ten times.

- Create triggers for repeating your affirmation (e.g., every time you sit down to a meal/when walking home from work/any repetitive action that works)

Affirmation	How do you feel after five minutes of repeating the affirmation? On a scale of 1–10 (1 good–10 very positive)
1. I am valuable as a person.	
2. I deserve love and respect.	
3. I am strong and independent.	
4. I am capable of having lasting relationships.	
5. I am lovable and I can give love in return.	
6. I am ready for love and intimacy.	

Check the ratings you have given yourself against each affirmation and choose the three that make you feel the most positive. Continue using those affirmations daily.

Mindfulness Meditation

These four exercises will help you practice mindfulness meditation while you get about your chores and daily schedule.

Mindfulness is to live in the moment and keep unruly thoughts from getting analyzed and judged. Such thinking is a trigger to ignite anger, sadness, and low self-confidence. Becoming mindful of your present situation is a good practice to avoid unnecessary thinking, which is often the crux of most problems people dealing with BPD experience.

Listed here are four simple exercises that will help you to practice being mindful just about anywhere. Each one is designed for you to find joy in your surroundings, learn to appreciate your worth, and stop negative thoughts from triggering your neurodivergent behavior.

Diligently practice the following exercises. You will not get it 100% in the beginning, but through persistence, you will soon master the skill.

Once you have had a chance to practice each mindfulness exercise, fill in the section below by answering how the experience helped you.

Exercise 3: Live for Simple Pleasures

Savor the moment. For example, if you are sitting on a park bench, savor that simple pleasure and enjoy being there. Do not entertain the random thoughts that flit through your mind; let them pass through. Find happiness in what you are doing at the moment.

Today, I practiced being mindful of simple pleasures. I felt...

Exercise 4: Open Up Your Senses

Pay attention to your surroundings with the help of your senses: touch, smell, sound, sight, and taste can amplify your experience and squash negative, nagging thoughts that keep creeping into your mind. If you are at a restaurant, use your senses to enjoy the meal, paying diligent attention to the texture, flavor, scent, and sight of the food. You will find that allowing your senses to take over an experience is very relaxing as you are not stressing your mind about negative thoughts.

Find activities to practice being aware:

- Go for a walk in the park after it rains.

- Make yourself a hot drink and become attuned to the flavor, heat, and feel of the drink to make it a sensory experience.

- Enjoy a long warm shower, especially if you suddenly feel disturbed and you need to get your emotions in check. This act will stimulate your senses and help distract you from the problem, causing you anxiety.

Today, I experienced the world through my senses. It made me feel...

Exercise 5: Become Accepting

Love yourself, accept your flaws, and acknowledge your achievements. Look for the positive of every negative thought you harbor. If you feel unworthy of love, ask yourself, "Why?" and then write down five reasons why you deserve love. Whenever you override a negative thought about yourself, you reinforce your sense of self-worth.

See yourself through the eyes of a friend or loving family member. You could ask them to write down five traits they love about you. Use those as affirmations to love yourself for who you are.

I love myself because…

Exercise 6: Practice Deep Breathing

Use deep breathing to help get out of a difficult situation. If you feel your emotions are rising and you may not be able to control an outburst, find a quiet corner and practice deep breathing.

- Take a deep breath through your nose all the way to feel your belly puff up. Count to three and breathe out from your mouth.

- Every time you breathe out, feel the stress dissipating and your emotional regulation growing.

- Practice about ten deep breaths until you feel in control and your emotional turmoil has subsided.

I used deep breathing to control my emotions. I was able to...

Emotional Freedom Tapping Meditation

Think of emotional freedom tapping meditation (EFT) as a way of opening up your mind to let the feelings of unworthiness and distrust flow out. When we are abandoned or rejected by someone—a lover, a caregiver, a close friend, and so on, the first thing we do is feel unworthy because the rejection evokes feelings of self-doubt:

- "Did I drive them away?"

- "It's all my fault."

- "I could have tried better."

Because you are dealing with BPD, you experience abandonment on a more painful level than others; therefore, they are pseudo-feelings augmented by your divergent mind that makes you overanalyze and judge yourself in a very negative manner.

So, you end up with a load of pessimistic thoughts that are built up inside your mind. Now, think of your mind as a dam, and those harmful thoughts are the pressure pressing against your mind, causing it to become flawed.

But you can stop the damage. One method is EFT: with it, you are creating an outlet for all those detrimental thoughts to flow out, easing the pressure and helping you to think clearly.

Let's begin.

What is EFT?

This method is used by people who want to control their minds and stop damaging thoughts and anxious behavior from taking over. The technique can also be used as a mediator to prevent stress and erratic emotions from taking over—you can practice EFT if you suddenly feel uncontrollable anger, panic, or any other distressing emotion taking over. It is a good tool to control your behavior and avoid giving in to triggers that set off your personality disorder.

The term "tapping" is used because EFT is practiced by tapping, with your fingertips, on certain pressure points on your head, torso, and hands. When practicing EFT, I like to envision a small hole opening up and all my negative emotions and thoughts flowing out.

Exercise 7: Practice EFT

Step 1: Close your eyes and recall a distressing event or issue. It does not have to be related to your abandonment fears; anything that ignites negative emotions in you can be used in EFT.

Step 2: How bad do you feel when you think of this issue?

Tick a box: one means it does not cause negative feelings in you, and ten means you are greatly affected by this issue.

1	2	3	4	5	6	7	8	9	10

My score is ………….. because the issue makes me feel…………………………………………….

Step 3: Write a statement about the issue positively.

Example 1: *"Although I feel let down by my partner leaving me, I will wake up stronger tomorrow; I will not let the rejection bring me down; I am special, and I am deserving of love and care."*

Example 2: *"I feel anxious about the new job interview I have tomorrow. I will be my best, and I will not let panic take over. I will face my challenge with confidence."*

My statement:

_____

_____

_____

Step 4: Now, take a deep breath, think of your issue, and repeat the statement you wrote above. As you do, use the tips of your fingers to tap non-stop on your palms under your little finger. Repeat the statement three times.

Step 5: Next, tap on other body parts as listed below. You must repeat the statement as you do so; it can be a shortened version of it.

Here's how to use the examples mentioned above.

Example 1: *"our relationship ended."*

Example 2: *"anxious about the interview."*

Tap on each of these points with your index and middle fingertips non-stop as you repeat your statement.

Let me explain using example 1: "our relationship ended"

Area to tap	Example Statement
1. The very top middle of your head.	"Our relationship ended"
2. The inner edge of your right or left eyebrow.	"Why did it happen that way?"
3. The outer end of your left or right eye.	"Could it be my fault?"
4. The bone under the left or right eye.	"Maybe the breakup was due to my partner's shortcomings."
5. The indented area right below your nose and above your upper lip.	"Does it matter whose fault it was? It's over?"
6. The middle area of your chin below your lower lip.	"Maybe I should move on and find a better love."
7. The inner edge of a collarbone, feel for the indent in the middle where the inner collarbone edges end.	"I deserve love and respect just as much as anyone else."
8. Four inches below one armpit.	"Maybe the breakup was a good thing?"

Now, stop and use step 2 to re-score the feeling associated with the issue

Continue to tap and repeat the order again, using the tapping rhythm to talk to yourself and gain more clarity on the issue that is bothering you until you get a lower score.

Keep analyzing and looking for positive outcomes that have evolved from the issue until you turn the anxiety into hope and a desire to move on from the feelings of hurt, rejection, panic, and so on.

Conquering Fear of Abandonment Through Clarity and Self-Reflection

Living in constant fear of another rejection, or the fear of being abandoned by someone you trust and look to for protection, are exhausting and damaging traits created through previous abandonment issues in people dealing with neurodivergent conditions.

Under each of the following self-reflection questions I have listed below, I want you to write your honest opinions and reasoning. And when you are done, go back and read them and then let's evaluate how you feel.

Exercise 8: Self-Reflection to Understand Your Fear of Abandonment

Find a quiet and calm place for this exercise. Practice deep breathing before you begin. Clear your mind and then reflect on each question before writing your answers.

I was abandoned by
They abandoned me by
As a result, I feel about relationships. And I believe people are
I protect myself from being abandoned again by And so, I engage in (being too suspicious/clingy/demanding/etc.)

Since I have experienced abandonment several times before, could it be that I may be contributing to the issue by

I dread not knowing the future because

And so, I manage my fears and my underlying insecurities of not knowing how new relationships are going to last by

Run through your answers and then write down any realizations you may have made. Describe any self-sabotaging behavior you may be repeating due to your insecurities.

I realized today that my fear of abandonment stems from

Exercise 9: Using Self-Reflectory Answers to Prevent the Past From Sabotaging the Present

1. How can I stop stressing over the outcome of future events over which I have no control because every time I start a new relationship or friendship, I sabotage it?

2. How can I change the way I think to stop stressing and trying to control future events—how can I learn to let go of my past fears and enjoy my new relationships?

3. I fear abandonment, but how many of those beliefs are true? Is it time I begin challenging some of those thoughts and fears as baseless?

———————◆———————

Distress Tolerance Techniques and How it Works

Distress tolerance describes someone's ability to handle a distressing situation without overreacting or feeling overwhelmed. In short, you can control your emotions despite the stressors. When dealing with BPD, distress triggers your fight or flight and freeze mode. Your parasympathetic nervous system kicks in and influences rapid changes like increased heart rate, erratic breathing, and sometimes feelings of nausea.

An effective remedy to gain control over these physical reactions is to stimulate the vagus nerve (VNS). Doing so offers an immediate respite where you can calm down and return your heart rate and breathing to resting mode. The vagus is the longest nerve that makes up your autonomic nervous system. Studies prove this stimulation has huge benefits to your nervous system and autonomic nervous system, which is what regulates your blood pressure, heart rate, and so on (Howland).

The benefits of using exercises to stimulate your vagus nerve:

- helps ease depression

- offers emotional regulation

- lowers heart rate

- relieves cluster headaches and migraine

TIPP is a DBT skill that you can use in four stages to help deal with anxiety, panic, and distress.

T=Temperature

I=Intense exercise

P=Paced breathing

P=Paired muscle relaxation

The distance tolerance techniques I want to introduce here are based on the theory of TIPP.

1. Cold water immersion therapy

2. Short bursts of exercise

3. Singing and humming

1. Cold Water Immersion for Distress Tolerance

Professional athletes indulge in ice baths as a relaxation method because lowering body temperatures helps improve emotional responses.

Cold water immersion therapy helps regulate heart rate and emotions and helps boost your parasympathetic nervous reaction. Cold water immersion can be a shock to the system at first and if practiced incorrectly or without being prepared. Therefore, before you go for the full immersion practice, these simpler therapies first, they too are effective against panic attacks and regulating mood.

Document your experience.

Exercise 10: Cold Water Face Immersion

Fill the sink or a basin (large enough to immerse your face) with water and ice cubes. Take five deep breaths to prepare yourself for the immersion, then on the last breath, plunge your face into the water. Hold it there with your eyes closed for a count of ten. The action immediately stimulates a response from the vagus nerve to regulate your heightened emotional response (Al Haddad et al.).

When you are not in a position for cold water face immersion, try these methods:

- Put the car's air conditioner on full force and hold your face to it.

- Take an ice cube and rub it around your face, including the back of your ears.

- Run cold water and splash your face for a quick and invigorating boost to your mood.

Exercise 11: Cold Shower

Cold showers are a good way to start your day invigorated. It boosts your circulation and will also alleviate any muscle soreness you may feel.

Ease into the experience. First, take your warm shower with the water temperature set at your regular range. Once done, turn the temperature down and stand under the cold spray of water for one or two minutes; don't push it beyond your comfort zone. Ease into the experience by extending the time you stand under the cold spray until you can enjoy a proper cold shower by starting on the cold setting.

Document your experience.

Exercise 12: Cold Water Bath

A cold water bath is one of the closest to the full experience of cold water immersion. Fill the tub and add ice cubes if the water is not icy cold. Again, ease into the experience. Do not attempt this alone; have someone monitor your time in the tub and help you out of the bath.

Never fully immerse your entire body at once, and do not remain for longer than five minutes. Prolonging the time you spend in the tub will not improve the experience.

Begin by easing your lower body into the tub, sit up and immerse your lower torso for about three minutes. It generally takes a minute for the shock factor to wear off, after which you can get more comfortable. Once the three minutes are up, immerse your upper body up to your shoulders for two minutes; do not immerse your head.

You can wear a long-sleeved shirt to help regulate your body temperature, have a hot drink immediately after, and dress in warm clothes. You will notice you feel more relaxed, and your body aches are reduced.

Document your experience.

_____

_____

_____

_____

_____

Exercise 13: Full Immersion

Swimming in a lake or open water offers full immersion and the benefits of cold water therapy as a mood regulator. Swim in the summer months, which you can do if you live or vacation close to a body of water. Do not dive right in; ease yourself into the water, especially if it is the ocean. It's better to wade in and let your body get accustomed to the cold before you start to swim.

- swim with a partner or inform family or friends of your plans

- wear a wetsuit when swimming in the ocean

- have warm clothes for after
- take along a warm drink and sweet to help replenish your blood sugar.

Document your experience.

_____

_____

_____

_____

_____

2. Short Bursts of Exercises for Distress Tolerance

Physical exertion stimulates your vagus nerve. Studies have proved that a fitness regime helps people with weakened parasympathetic responses, like those dealing with epilepsy, to improve their mood, and control heart rhythm, thus stimulating the vagus nerve response (Yuen and Sander).

The exercises offered here will help reduce your sympathetic nervous response, regulate your emotions, and control your cardiac response.

Exercise 14: Intense Workout

If sudden panic, anger, frustration, etc. grips you and you feel you are going to vent, or lose control of your emotions, aim that intense build-up of emotional energy at an equally intense action because increasing levels of oxygen in your system help to reduce levels of stress, plus no one who is physically exhausted has the energy to be emotionally upset.

Here are some suggestions.

- jumping jacks: Find a quiet corner of your home or even your office where you can indulge in a few jumps to get your heart pumping from physical exertion and not heightened emotions.

- sprint: So, you are worried about an impending exam, and you feel panic building up. Put on your trainers and sprint a few blocks around your house until you are both exhausted and calmer.

- swim: Join a club, or you may own a pool; either way, a few intense laps will get your heart pumping and dispel those anxious feelings. A few fast-paced laps regularly will help you to regulate your moods and enjoy a calmer personality.

Document your experience.

_____

_____

_____

_____

Exercise 15: Neck Stretches to Stimulate the Vagus Nerve Response

This one is excellent for relieving yourself of sudden tension or panic. The activity helps to flex the sternocleidomastoid, which is a muscle located on one side of your neck, where, when tension builds, it causes problems like migraine. Stretching this muscle stimulates the vagus nerve.

- Sit comfortably with your back straight.

- Practice three long deep breaths; in from your mouth to your belly and out from your nostrils.

- On the third breath: Place the palm of your right hand on your head and gently guide your head to bend toward the right shoulder until your right ear touches it. While looking up, gently breathe and hold the pose for a count of 30 seconds, and as you exhale, straighten your head.

- Take three deep breaths.

- Now repeat the same by placing your left hand on your head and lowering your left ear toward the left shoulder.

You should feel an immediate shift of tension as you do this.

Document your experience.

_____

_____

_____

Exercise 16: Stretching Your Torso

Twisting your torso is another exercise to stimulate your vagus nerve response and a good method to feel relaxed and more flexible.

- Sit down on the ground, floor, or chair.

- Place the palm of your right hand on the outer corner of your left thigh.

- Bend your left arm behind you.

- Now turn your neck to look over your left shoulder.

- Inhale, straighten your spine, and rotate your neck and body further, enjoying the feeling of stretching and relaxation it brings.

3. Singing, Humming, and Exercising Your Vocal Cords for Vagus Nerve Stimulation

Connected to your vagus nerve, your vocal cords, when activated, can stimulate vagus nerve response. Any type of vocal activity, including chanting, humming, singing, and even gargling, will ignite stimulation.

The following simple exercises will help you to use your vocal cords VNS.

Exercise 17: Gargling With Water

- Make it a practice to use water and gargle twice a day when brushing your teeth. First thing in the morning and the last activity at night.

- Gargle for 30 to 60 seconds.

- Make as much noise as possible and feel the vibration in your throat.

  Document your experience.

_____

_____

_____

Exercise 18: Chanting

Enjoy the vibrating melodious chant as practiced in yoga for VNS. I recommend using this vocal therapy to ease your mind and stimulate your nervous response at the same time.

- Sit comfortably on the floor and deep breathe for one minute.

- Close your eyes and concentrate on your breaths, puffing out your stomach.

- Breathe out and imagine the stress flowing out with that breath.

- Breathe in and then begin the chant.

- You can use the traditional "om" chant.

- Chant loud enough so you feel the vibration. This vibration can help clear your sinuses, eases cardiovascular conditions, and helps you to relax. Above all, chanting and vibration stimulate your vagus nerve and your parasympathetic response (Inbaraj et al.).

Document your experience.

_____

_____

_____

_____

Exercise 19: Singing

Whether we sing off-key or like Celine Dion, it does not matter. Singing is food for the soul and makes us feel good. And it is scientifically proven as more than a "feel-good" exercise as it helps with the dysfunction of your autonomic nervous system, helps to improve blood pressure, heart rate, and also an electrodermal activity that helps deal with cognitive stress (Ellis and Thayer).

Turn on your favorite track and sing along. Do this whenever you feel your emotional triggers are taking over.

Here are some suggestions.

- Sing in your vehicle while driving to and from work; it is ideal for destressing after a tough day at the office dealing with difficult situations.

- Singing in the shower, especially if you are taking a cold shower in the morning, is a good method to prepare yourself emotionally to confidently face the day.

- Hum to yourself while commuting with your headphones on and your favorite track playing.

Train yourself to use music as a way of escaping a build-up of pressure. In time, humming or singing a song softly will become an automatic response whenever you feel your emotions and behavior slipping out of control.

Document your experience.

_____

_____

_____

_____

_____

Exercise 20: Laughing

Laughter automatically makes us feel good; the sound and the vibration a good guffaw causes in your vocal muscles easily stimulate your vagus nerve response. Here are some suggestions for using laughter as a self-soothing technique and means of escapism and relaxation techniques.

- Find happiness in little things, avoid being reserved, and choose to laugh out loud whenever you get the chance. Gravitate toward people who make you laugh—cheerful family members and friends.

- Download a few funny movies and silly clips you find funny to your smartphone. Use these to destress in the office or anywhere else you may feel overwhelmed.

- At the end of a particularly stressful day, choose to relax with a good comedy, a series on the television, or a feel-good, funny movie.

Do not give into isolation, as it aggravates stress. Become aware of your situation and find ways to spend time with people you love; call a friend, go out to a public area and become a part of society, and try to find reasons to smile and laugh at everyday events. It is not easy at first, but through perseverance and understanding your triggers, you can learn to avoid placing yourself in situations that are harmful to you emotionally, mentally, and physically.

Document your experience.

_____

_____

_____

_____

_____

Exercises for Interpersonal Effectiveness

Interpersonal effectiveness, which is how your social and interaction skills are defined, works on three factors:

1. Becoming skilled at getting others to supply your wants and needs.

2. Strengthening good relationships and letting go of harmful liaisons.

3. Learning to be accepting and understanding compromise in a relationship.

Relationships are based on a give-and-take scenario; it is about supplementing each other, respecting each other's individuality, and accepting compromise to find balance.

There are times you may be wrong and unreasonable; there are times you may have to be accepting of the other person's needs and wants even if you don't agree 100%—walk the middle path and meet them halfway so you do not come across as needy, unreasonable, and sometimes selfish.

- "How many times have I been unreasonably angry with my partner to find that they can see beyond my weaknesses to love me unconditionally—was I able to do the same?"

- "Was it my persistent and unreasonable expectations that finally drove them away?"

- "Could I have been more accepting and open to change myself? Changes I envisioned for the other person."

It's easy to lose yourself in our over-analytical behavior, to become blind to our abnormal expectations of other people to the point that we see ourselves as "perfect" through rose-tinted glasses.

1. Being Effectively Objective

By safeguarding your self-respect and rights, you can successfully become objective; thus making sure your legitimate rights and the right to refuse to do what you dislike are met, as well as having an opportunity to be able to resolve a conflict within your relationship, make sure your opinion is valued and to succeed at getting someone to do what you want.

Exercise 21: Obtaining Your Needs From Another

Answer the following questions to assert the relationship in your eyes. Be honest about your expectations and what you need from the other person.

Q1: What are my expectations from this relationship? What do I want as a positive result?

_____

_____

_____

_____

_____

Q2: What must I do to get those results? What kind of action works?

_____

_____

_____

Exercise 22: Improving and Making Your Relationship Last

To make a relationship last and get over repetitive patterns of abandonment, you need to work on your relationships. To do so, there are truths that you must reveal through self-evaluation. It's not easy to come to terms with some realities, but it's important to do so and answer the following questions as positively and truthfully as possible to help yourself.

Your ultimate goals in making a relationship last should be based on the following.

- Establishing goals and trying to maintain them for the greater good of making your relationship last.

- Cordially maintaining your behavior toward the other person, ensuring they continue to respect and love you.

- Make an effort to sustain relationships that are important to you.

The following questions will help you to ascertain how much effort and influence you exert toward the health of a relationship.

Q1: How will the other person think of me if this relationship ends? It doesn't matter if I didn't get what I expected from the relationship. What matters is the other person's perception of me as a person.

I believe they think of me as:

_____

_____

_____

_____

They have these thoughts of me because:

_____

_____

_____

Q2: I want the relationship to last, to expand into a deeper partnership. Therefore, I must do the following:

_____

_____

_____

_____

Exercise 23: Working on My Self-Respect

Self-respect is the base on which your emotional stability stands. Loving and respecting yourself is what matters above all. Once you are emotionally happy and content with who you are, you can love another person unconditionally and more openly.

Self-respect means:

- respecting and maintaining your ethics and values

- behaving in a manner that instills confidence in yourself

- feeling good about yourself and your morals

To further these goals, answer these questions in a self-analytical manner that helps you to delve deeper into your perception of yourself.

Q1: How do I want to continue feeling about myself even after abandonment? Even if I did not get what I wanted from the relationship?

_____

_____

_____

_____

Q2: What can I do if I don't feel good about myself? How must I think to have a better opinion of myself, stop selling myself short, and realize that I deserve to be loved?

---

2. Validation

An important aspect of successful interpersonal effectiveness is validation. What is validation?

- It's about verification, seeking facts to validate the situation, and looking for the truth in the circumstance the other person is facing.

- Realizing that someone's thoughts, emotions, and behavior are connected to actions, reasons, and causes, therefore, their actions are understandable.

- However, validating and accepting is wrong if you try to validate invalid causes. And trying to validate causes you are not agreeable to.

When you make an effort to validate, you are strengthening your relationship by extending respect to the wants and needs of the other person. You can strengthen your bond and relationship by alleviating unreasonable anger and the need to be "right." This helps you to compromise and deal with problems positively, thus avoiding a pattern of losing the relationship.

Validation is sometimes about meeting in the middle; it can be about factors you dislike, and it's about respecting the other persons, emotions, opinions, beliefs, and ideals about certain situations.

Exercise 24: How to Skillfully Practice Positive Validation

Validation is about offering the other person your respect and understanding. Therefore, make an effort to maintain the following guidelines when dealing with another person. It may not be easy at first, but striving to follow these guidelines will help you to change your responses and behavior to reflect respect toward the other person.

1. Offer Undivided Attention

When you validate the other person, make sure your actions and body language resonate with it.

What to do:

a. Observe, pay attention, and listen attentively; nod your head to show acknowledgment.

b. Look them in the eye when they are talking, giving them 100% attention.

c. Show your interest through your reactions; smile for happy statements, frown for distressing ones, and so on.

Acting and Thinking Dialectically:

- There are always two sides to a story. Ask yourself,
  "What am I missing?"

- Stop thinking in extremes. Drop the word "never" and add the word "sometimes" to your thinking process.

  "*Sometimes* I could be wrong to judge."

Today, I was able to practice undivided attention when:

_____

_____

I reflected on what was said and was accepting of the correction:

_____

_____

I was able to read between the lines and realized what was unsaid:

_____

_____

2. Do Not Judge

You can acknowledge that you understood by repeating what was said by the other person. Listen—do not jump to defend yourself, criticize, belittle, or try to offer your point of reasoning. Before you respond, examine the facts and try to see them from their point of view.

"Are you upset because you think I excluded you on purpose? Is that the reason?"

Acting and Thinking Dialectically

- Avoid passing blame. Instead, analyze how behaviors are affected by events that reoccur due to specific causes and realize they are not worthy of passing blame.

Today, I was able to let go of blame and look at the issue in a more positive light for both of us: (Explain your experience and the realization you made.)

_____

_____

_____

_____

_____

_____

3. Become Intuitive

This means being able to read body language. By paying attention, you will be able to understand what is being said through a person's body language and not verbally. Their eyes, stance, and actions are speaking to you—pay attention.

Acting and Thinking Dialectically

- Observe how your actions and reactions affect the other person.

For example, you may ask someone to join you for a movie after work, but if you notice them suddenly avoiding looking at you and struggling to give you an answer, it could mean they already have plans or they are in a hurry to get home, etc. At those times, use your understanding to extend a respite to the other person.

You could say something like:

"Or maybe we could take a rain check when you are free; it's quite alright."

Today, I used my intuitive powers to help my friend/lover avoid an uncomfortable situation. It did not make me feel as though they were abandoning me because I was able to understand from their point of view.

(Write the experience here and your realizations.)

_____

_____

_____

_____

_____

_____

4. Be Fair in Your Treatment of the Other Person

Do not try to belittle the other person. See them as your equal and not as weaker, more sensitive, or less capable than you. When you view them in this negative sense, you are placing less importance on who they are as an individual, which can affect the health of your relationship with them.

Acting and Thinking Dialectically

- Treat people the same way you want to be treated

- Stop looking for differences between yourself and people; instead, look for similar traits, so that you do not alienate yourself as a victim but see flaws and strengths as common characteristics.

Today, I was able to connect and form a stronger bond because I stopped trying to be superior.

(Write the experience here and your realizations.)

_____

_____

_____

_____

Exercise 25: Confirming My Validations and Their Effects

- Write about a situation where you didn't judge someone. Look at the overall circumstances and put yourself in a similar situation.

- Write two validating statements of encouragement you made to someone in the past week.

1.

2.

- Who did you validate, and what was the outcome?

3. Failure to Establish Essential Boundaries in a Relationship

To enjoy feeling good about yourself and your worth within a relationship, it is important to establish healthy boundaries—they lead to healthy relationships that have the potential to last.

However, you may have a pattern of avoiding establishing boundaries; instead, you make demands that often get ignored, leading to frustration and low self-esteem because you feel your needs and opinions are disrespected.

Why *do* you not establish healthy boundaries?

If you take the time to analyze your situation, you will realize your reluctance to establish boundaries is based on fear. A fear that is manifested in the dread of abandonment. In simpler terms, you fear establishing boundaries for fear of facing abandonment yet again. You may be too timid, fear conflict, and favor pleasing the other person above respecting your needs.

- "What if I am rejected?"

- "Will I make them angry by telling them what I want?"

- "How do I deal with them saying no?"

That type of thinking is not foolproof, and soon cracks will start forming in your relationship because you will start feeling oppressed.

Exercise 26: Learning to Establish Boundaries

Answer the following questions as truthfully as possible and use them to help yourself find successful methods to create boundaries within your relationship.

1. How can I express my emotions and thoughts without being judged?

2. If I say "no" to what I dislike, how will that response be accepted, and how do I assert myself without creating conflict?

_____

_____

_____

_____

_____

3. What are the common goals and interests we share? How can I use them to create a mutual understanding of my likes and dislikes in a non-aggressive scenario?

_____

_____

_____

_____

_____

4. How do I want to spend my free time? Am I doing what I like, or am I simply trying to keep everyone else happy?

_____

_____

_____

5. Are my opinions valued? Am I trusted? How can I establish trust and value, and how much am I willing to tolerate?

6. How do I introduce cooperation as a successful tool for establishing and accepting boundaries?

If you find the answers are more negative, it's time to ascertain your needs. These questions are not meant to create conflict within your relationship; they are meant to be a way for you to face your realities within the relationship.

The Three Pillars of Establishing Healthy Boundaries

Establish your boundaries on the following principles, thus defining yourself.

- Personal values are established by independent individuals who make up a healthy relationship. What are the core values that define you? How important is it to maintain them? Likewise, are the values that can be re-established? Principles that can be relooked at for the greater good of the relationship.

- Make sure it's a relationship that honors and defends your personal needs, thus, making sure your individuality is not compromised. Look within your relationship. Have you made compromises that go against your core values? Have you communicated your values, or have you been inconsistent with your values? If you have not been clear about your personal needs, you cannot expect positive results.

- Ensure boundaries are communicated effectively using verbal and non-verbal methods that are neither destructive nor offensive. Here it's about practicing what you preach. Give the same as what you expect in return and lead by example. You cannot expect to gain respect and trust if you do not offer the same.

4. Working on Emotional Regulation

Our emotional triggers are a safety net. At first, anxiety helped our ancestors stay safe and alert. Our emotional triggers instigate certain responses that can help us. In the case of dealing with BPD, it's common to face emotional regulation disorder where you are not in control of the processing of your emotions methodically. It is a dysfunction within the system that prevents proper process, regulation, and management of your emotions.

Emotional regulation is the modifier that helps us maintain a balance between the many emotions we face daily.

Being mindful is one of the most successful tools for emotional regulation. The following exercises are based on helping you gain control of your emotional mechanism whenever you face triggers and feel you are losing control. Practice them when you are at home to become versed in the techniques and you will be able to adopt the exercises when the need arises.

Exercise 27: Breathing Drills to Regulate Your Emotions

1. Shifting

Become aware of your body's reaction to inhaling and exhaling.

- Sit comfortably, and place one hand on your stomach and one on your chest. Now start deep breathing.

- With each inhale, watch how your hands rise and fall; the hand on your stomach will move out while the hand on your chest moves up.

- Exhale and notice the differences.

- Continue to do so, focusing on your body's reaction to your breathing and learning to focus on your body.

2. Counting

Sit or stand quietly for a minute and try to still your thoughts. Then count to five and inhale. Count to seven and exhale. Repeat the exercise until you become focused on the rhythm you have created as you breathe.

3. Relaxation

This one should be your go-to tool for dealing with sudden stress and anxiety. Practice deep breathing by finding a quiet corner. Breathe in and hold your breath for a count of five, then breathe out to a count of seven. Repeat the exercise until you feel a sense of calm washing over you.

Exercise 28: Self-Awareness

This technique works on naming your thoughts, linking them to the causes, and coming to terms with understanding your emotional triggers.

Start the practice as a daily assertion of your emotions. Then, at the end of the day, you can gather your thoughts and emotions and use them to understand your feelings.

Date:	The strongest emotion I felt/am feeling today is:	It was caused by: (person or circumstance)	I dealt with it by:	When dealing with the emotion, I felt:

Using the Exercises in This Chapter

There are 28 exercises in this chapter designed to help you deal with abandonment-related emotions, thoughts, and behavior. Start by choosing the exercise that appeals to you the most. You are not expected to follow all of them. It's alright to practice one or two and come back to the others at a later date.

Journal Your Progress

Start your journey with DBT by chronicling your experiences and progress in a journal. Make it a habit to write a few minutes a day; this does not have to be whole sentences. Your journal can be made up of words, thoughts, cartoons, and caricatures. It reflects how you are dealing with your emotions and behavior and should make sense to you; that is all that matters. Use it as a tool to help you analyze your thoughts, emotions, and behavior. To rethink your thought process, to accept when you are wrong, and to change your perspective where needed.

While dealing with abandonment issues, it is also important to find ways to strengthen your relationships. Let's look at how in the next chapter.

Chapter TWO

What to Do When You Can't Establish Healthy Relationships

I saw that you were perfect, and so I loved you. Then I saw that you were not perfect and I loved you even more.

- Angelita Lim

Hilary had no trouble attracting partners; the trouble was keeping them. Her relationships were always intense, passionate, and perfect—at first. Then they would start to change; her partners would become cold and distant. She would struggle to maintain trust and a balance of understanding. She would end up dealing with her heightened emotions, which caused her to judge find fault and overreact, the wedge that caused her relationships to end badly. The repetitive pattern that followed each failed relationship was exhaustive, and Hilary was ready to give up or love until she decided to investigate and seek help. She was diagnosed with borderline personality disorder. The pieces of the puzzle started to fall into place, and Hilary could finally begin to heal.

Being Mindful of Your Relationships

The DBT approach to practicing mindfulness works on three theories.

1. The reasonable mind is based on facts, is analytical and colder in coming to conclusions.

2. The emotional mind is based on sensations and emotions where passion and impulse rule.

3. The wise mind encompasses all possible stages of deduction; it is intuitive, unpressured, and relies on reflective thought and the sixth sense.

The WHAT and HOW Skills of DBT

In DBT, mindfulness is practiced by fine-tuning WHAT and HOW skills.

WHAT skills are focused on being mindful of the present situation:

- being observant

- describing the situation

- participation in the situation

- how intentional you are toward the outcome

HOW skills represent the main attributes you afford the circumstance and are therefore based on:

- being non-judgmental

- paying 100% attention to the moment and practicing your WHAT skills

- being effective with your observations

Exercise 29: Practice Your WHAT and HOW Skills

What do you observe?

_____

_____

_____

Describe in words what you experience:

_____

_____

_____

Become a participant in the experience here, and describe how you feel:

_____

_____

_____

Make a note of the judgment; describe why and what influenced your verdict:

_____

_____

_____

Find one event in this experience to focus on; what is it?

_____

_____

_____

What is the most effective solution to the experience—not what you think is right, but what is essential:

_____

_____

_____

Find similar situations to analyze in this manner until you realize the triggers that cause you to become critical and judgmental. Stick to the WHAT and HOW theories and use your journal to analyze the situation. An experience put down in words can take on a whole new perspective. Look for solutions to your relationship problems that are not influenced by judgmental impulses.

Self-Soothing to Manage Distressing Situations

Learn to calm your mind before you let the rising panic/fear/anger engulf you and take over. Often relationships are driven apart through hasty words and actions that cannot be taken back; that may be a pattern for you since your BPD is a trigger for rash reactions.

Deep breathing is a good technique to help you to calm down when you sense your emotions are starting to boil over. Think of a baby who suddenly stops wailing when a soother is placed in their mouth; find your soother. Sharpen your senses, and you will find a way to self-soothe and calm your emotions.

The raisin technique is highly successful in helping people sharpen their five senses. Once done, you will find that simply looking out the window and treating your senses to what you are observing in the environment helps to transport your mind away from the distress-causing situation to a calmer plain.

Exercise 30: The Raisin Technique for Mindfulness

This technique helps you to practice mindfulness even when engaged in daily tasks we need not pay attention to: brushing teeth, washing dishes, etc. The technique works by taking a single raisin and observing it.

Use your senses:

- touch
- sight
- smell
- taste
- sound

If raisins are not your preference, choose another food type for the experiment; a grape, strawberry, a single piece of macaroni from the bowl you are about to eat, etc.

I will use a raisin as an example to describe the exercise.

Step 1: Pick up a single raisin, hold it between your fingers, turn it around, and look at it. Become aware of how odd this action feels because you would generally pop the raisin in your mouth and eat.

Step 2: Observe that plain old raisin like never before; see it in a new light, really look at it. The wrinkled skin, the color when the lights hit, and how small it is. Become mindful of how that raisin *really* looks.

Step 3: Now feel the raisin; is the skin smooth or rough? When you press it, how firm or soft is it Is it squishy or firm?

Step 4: Smell the raisin; you may never have noticed its subtle scent before. Hold it to your nose and breathe in the smell. Use your sense of smell 100% to gather its essence.

Step 5: Gently place the raisin on your tongue. Now feel its texture as you roll it around in your mouth. Smooth, soft, wrinkly? Do not chew it. Simply get a feel of it in your mouth.

Step 6: Very slowly bite into the raisin. Become aware of the sudden release of flavor; what can you taste? Tear apart the raisin and feel the flesh inside, and at the same time become aware of the saliva being secreted in your mouth. As you chew, can you observe the sound your mouth is making as the saliva mixes in with the raisin?

Step 7: Become aware of the urge to swallow the raisin, but don't. Roll it around, and notice how your tongue behaves toward digesting the food. Now slowly swallow the bits, and feel them slide down your throat. How is your tongue aiding the action, and does your throat make a sound as the food slides down?

Step 8: Observe; how does your mouth taste now? What is the aftertaste? Do you feel as though you want to eat more or have a drink? Can you feel a difference in your throat and stomach? You have never eaten this mindfully before; therefore, can you observe new sensations in your stomach and mouth as a result?

- My observation of the entire experiment, I have never eaten this mindfully before, it helped me to become aware of my sense of smell, taste, touch, sight, and sound: (Write your experience here)

_____

_____

_____

_____

_____

_____

Exercise 31: Using Mindfulness for Self-Soothing

Use this technique in conjunction with what you learned through the raisin experiment: focusing on your senses.

Stand at the window or step outside and think about nothing except observing your surroundings.

- Look—observe your surroundings and become aware of what you see; trees swaying in the breeze, people passing by, a leaf on the ground. Become totally aware of your surroundings as though you are looking at the details of a painting.

- Feel—the wind as it caresses your face, is it chilly, or can you feel the warmth of the sun on your skin?

- Smell—is it after a rain, and does everything smell fresh? Can you smell food from a nearby restaurant, fumes from vehicles, scents from plants, etc?

- Touch—what's near you? The windowpane, does it feel cold, a tree, what is the texture? Touch objects close to you and feel a connection.

Now close your eyes and try to remember all you just saw and felt. And realize how the technique helped you to become mindful of your surroundings. At that moment no other emotions clouded your mind.

Write down your thoughts and emotions. How did you feel after this exercise:

_____

_____

_____

_____

Practice this technique and use it to self-soothe when the need arises. Train your mind to slip into that calmer plain away from the pain and triggers that you fear will cause you to become emotional.

Learn Guided Meditation

Our minds can't stop wondering; it reviews the present, past, and future and at times, can become stifling and overbearing. Mindfulness helps you to hold those thoughts long enough for you to take a breath and refresh. But those same thoughts can be intrusive, and some of us find practicing mindfulness difficult because of our heightened emotions. However, it's not impossible to become mindful of a thought long enough to change its perspective.

The following guide will help you to get started, to get a grip on your wandering thoughts, and pin them down long enough to give your mind a breather to understand the confusions you are dealing with in your relationship.

Exercise 32: Learning to Relax and Practice Mindfulness to Improve Your Relationships

Find a quiet, comfortable place and use the following exercise as a guide.

I suggest you read each of these steps aloud as you record yourself doing so. Then close your eyes and play back the recording; listen to your voice (there is no one you trust more).

Listen to yourself and follow the guide.

1. Sit down or lie down and practice deep breathing.

2. Let go of the tension in your shoulders; let them slump.

3. Relax your body and feel as though a weight has left you.

4. As you settle down and calm your body, sense a flow of energy. You will notice your hands feel warm, and there will be a tingling sensation.

5. Deep breathe for a minute. Give into the sensation of each breath as you inhale and exhale. Feel the tension leave your body with each breath you exhale.

6. Next, use your imagination and see yourself walking in a beautiful forest.

7. It's evening, and the sun is casting shadows all around as golden light pierces through the trees.

8. Hear the birds chirping and the wind rustling the trees, and as you walk, feel the ground below your feet.

9. As you walk, you suddenly come to a clearing and see a pretty patch of grass. You sit at the edge of a log and look across the field.

10. Then you sense someone close by and turn to see a deer coming to the clearing. And the deer says, "How are you?"

11. You are very surprised at a talking deer, but you answer. "I'm good, I just came for a walk to think. I fear my relationship may not last."

12. "Aha, I can help you there; what's on your mind?" says the deer.

13. You think it's really odd that a deer is offering you relationship advice, but you decide to try it, so you start to confide about what's good and bad in your relationship.

14. The deer listens patiently until you are done and says, "Well, everything you pay more attention to in a relationship gets highlighted more and becomes real."

15. "You can focus on what irritates you and scares you, or you can focus on the feeling of love and happiness your relationship brings."

16. Now, think about all the good things in your relationship. Take your time to do so.

17. Think about these for a minute.

18. After you tell the deer all the good things in your relationship, he asks you to name one thing that annoys you. Name it.

19. After you do, think about that annoying factor; is it bad, or can it help you to be selfless enough to overcome it?

20. Reflect on these thoughts for a minute until you realize that the annoying factor is not really an issue but a way to make your relationship stronger because you can learn to be accepting of behavior you don't agree with.

21. When you tell this to the deer, it says, "Do you see that, in your relationship, your thoughts are responsible for how you feel? You can control the direction they take and use them to fine-tune and fix problems from your end. You can control your thoughts and not the other person's. But your contribution to the relationship can greatly influence how and what the other person feels when you project positivity and appreciation.

22. That annoying thought is only annoying if you allow it to be so. See it in a new light by thinking 'maybe.'

23. Maybe my partner was not arguing but what they wanted was important to them. Maybe I overreacted? I could have been more sensitive to their needs instead of thinking they were being selfish about mine.

24. Become accepting and change your initial reaction to the situation. Use your critical thinking abilities. We all possess this skill, which allows us to take a negative factor and make it positive simply by changing how we view a situation.

25. The deer tells you to reflect on these new ideas for a minute.

26. Do so.

27. Then you hear the deer say, "Another point I want you to reflect on is that your relationship is not based on how much you think the other person loves you, but on how much you love yourself." Self-love and appreciation are the keys to confidence and happiness because when you love yourself, you can love others unconditionally.

28. Take a minute to think about this. How much importance do you give yourself in the relationship?

29. Appreciate yourself, see how you can improve yourself to become truly happy, and not rely on the other person to make you feel whole and appreciated.

30. Realize that you are responsible for how you feel, just like you are responsible for what you think is annoying or not in your relationship.

31. You smile at the deer because you suddenly realize that a relationship is only as successful as you make it; the other person has nothing to do with how you feel. You can look for positives and not hang on to negatives.

32. You thank the deer and head back, and as you do, you reflect on your relationship, and suddenly you see things from a totally different perspective.

33. What changed?

34. Nothing! Except for the way you think.

35. Reflect on this and become mindful of how much power you possess within your MIND to make a relationship last or end.

My reflections on this meditation exercise:

_____

_____

_____

_____

I am stronger than I believe I am, and I have the power to make my relationship a success because:

_____

_____

_____

_____

The Stop Skill—DBT Distress Tolerance Skills to Prevent Reacting to External Stimuli

The stop skill can be used to avoid causing damage to your relationship instigated by external stimuli. The external stimuli can be a reaction from a lover, friend, family member, and so on, which causes your emotions to get out of hand because your BPD makes it hard to regulate your emotions. Sometimes you may feel totally out of control, as though you are standing on the outside watching yourself overact but helpless to stop.

The S.T.O.P skill is a good tool for averting such a crisis caused by external stimulation of your emotional responses.

Exercise 33: STOP SKILL

STOP Skill For DBT Distress Tolerance	
S = STOP	• Avoid reacting to the situation; remain in control.
T= Take a Step Back	• Step back. • Don't act impulsively. • Stop and take a deep breath.
O= Observe	• What thoughts are running through your mind? • How do you feel? • What is the other person doing?
P = Proceed	• Become mindful; you are better than this. • Remind yourself of your goals. • Remind yourself of your dreams. • Walk away.

Today I practiced my STOP skill, and I was able to control my emotions to a great extent. I feel:

Healthy Distractions for Distress Tolerance

Distractions help you to overcome having to deal with distressing situations by diluting your emotional reaction and attention toward the event. We spoke about using mindfulness as a distraction to prevent your emotions from spiraling out of control. Healthy distractions work the same.

- Distractions can be exercises you attempt on your own.
- Distractions you enjoy by being with a partner, friend, or family member.

Distractions I Can Enjoy On My Own

Choose one of the following exercises and practice it every time you are distressed and need emotional regulation.

Exercise 34: Become a Photographer

I am not talking about skilled photographers or people who are experts at selfies. It does not matter if you have no aesthetic eye, invest in a digital camera or use your phone, and get out there to let nature and people distract you.

Here are some ideas for you to get started with photography as a distraction from a stressful situation.

a. Photograph the sunset in its many shades, or the sky and shapes of clouds, puddles left by the rain, or trash being blown by the wind on a busy street and son, and these are analytical objects you can photograph to look at and feel distracted about your emotional turmoil.

b. Photograph people rushing home at the end of the day.

c. Photograph the city skyline from your office window.

d. Photograph your hands, feet, and face so you can analyze the expressions there.

Note: Today, I was upset,

_____

_____

But I took my camera out and was able to capture several insightful images that made me happy because looking at them made me feel:

_____

_____

_____

_____

Exercise 35: Write a Letter

There are several benefits to writing a letter; it can be addressed to the person who deeply hurt you because putting your thoughts down on paper makes you look at the problem from a whole new perspective. You will be able to express yourself in a new context. Let out all the emotional turmoil you feel. It is up to you whether you wish to give the person the letter or not. Writing the letter is what's important.

Note: Today I was deeply hurt by...

I am writing this letter to let them know how it affected me:

_____

_____

Exercise 36: Make a List of Places You Want to Visit

Daydreaming about exotic places you want to visit is certainly a good distraction to turn a negative emotion around. You can draw up a list of places you want to visit and then choose to update an itinerary list for each destination whenever you need a distraction from your emotional turmoil.

Note: My Ultimate Bucket List of Holiday Destinations:

Today I am going to explore the attractions in ....

Here's what I plan to do when I get there:

How do I feel emotionally after writing about my dream destination?

Exercise 37: Call a Friend, Family Member

Often, a phone call to a friend or loved family member can make us feel loved, appreciated, and needed. It is the perfect elixir to make us feel good and forget the hurt we are enduring. Call someone you haven't spoken to for a while. When you have loads to catch up on, you forget about the distress you are feeling and simply sink into that marvelous feeling of nostalgia.

Note: Today I was upset, so I called...

It felt really good to reminisce, and we talked a lot about old times. It made me feel:

_____

_____

_____

_____

_____

Exercise 38: Activities I Can Engage in When I Need a Distraction from a Stressful Situation

Here are more activities to redirect your emotions and thoughts and create a distraction for your mind to let go of the building anxiety.

Exercise 39: Indulge in a Memory Game.

This can be anything: a picture in your home or office, a scene outside the window, etc. Look at the object/scene for five seconds, then close your eyes and recapture the image in your mind. Then write down what you remember.

_____

_____

_____

_____

Exercise 40: Center Your Thoughts on a Personal Statement.

My name is…I live in…my favorite color is…today is a…(day of the week) in the month of…right now the time is…and so on. Broaden the statement you are making and immerse your thoughts in what you are saying at the moment, creating a good distraction from what was upsetting for you.

Note: Today, I practiced this exercise. It helped because:

_____

_____

_____

_____

_____

_____

Exercise 41: Use Number Distractions

The theory of using numbers to distract your mind works for dialectical behavior too. A particularly distressing situation can be squashed by distracting your mind. Counting to a hundred using your fingers, reciting a table, or counting back from 100 are all good stimuli for your mind and distractions for your stress.

Note: Using numbers is a good distraction as I am able to:

_____

_____

_____

_____

_____

_____

_____

_____

Exercise 42: Visualize Getting Rid of the Stress

Use your mind to leave or get rid of the distressing situation. Use your imagination to visualize the following when you are experiencing emotional disjointedness.

- Imagine yourself walking away from the situation; "adios," you say as you wave goodbye.

- There is someone yelling at you, and you are getting distressed, but you stop and, in your mind, you have turned your back on them.

- Suddenly, you jump into a lake and swim away.

- You hang on to a vine, like Tarzan, and swing far from them.

- You hop on your bike and cycle as fast as you can in the opposite direction.

You can do all this imaginative walking away while in that situation by letting your mind slip away and escape to freedom.

Note: I tried this exercise today when:

_____

It made me feel:

_____

_____

_____

_____

_____

Distress Tolerance Distractions to Engage With a Friend or Partner

Socializing is one of the tools you can use to create a distraction from stressful situations. We explored activities you can indulge in alone. Now let's look at activities you can enjoy with a partner or friend.

Choose Distress Tolerance Exercises to Enjoy With a Friend or Partner

Exercise 43: Join a Dance Class

A friend or lover will make an ideal dance partner. Dancing is an excellent exercise to distract emotions and thoughts and encourages the release of feel-good chemicals like serotonin, dopamine, and oxytocin.

Document your experience

_____

_____

_____

_____

_____

_____

_____

_____

_____

_____

_____

Exercise 44: Hike Together

Join a neighborhood hike club or engage in the activity with an enthusiastic friend or partner. Not only will you enjoy being outdoors, but you are also exercising your body and stimulating your senses. Perfect distractions for a dysfunctional mind prone to overreactions.

Document your experience

_____

_____

_____

_____

_____

_____

_____

_____

_____

Exercise 45: Couples Yoga

Yoga is great for learning to center yourself. Practicing the technique with a partner will help with both creating a distraction and a bond.

Document your experience

_____

_____

_____

_____

_____

_____

_____

_____

_____

Exercise 46: Play a Sport

Tennis, basketball, and so on are contact sports that let you sweat it out, distract your mind, and enjoy the company of someone else.

Document your experience

_____

_____

_____

_____

_____

_____

_____

_____

_____

Exercise 47: Attend a Community Project

Head over to the local soup kitchen, organize a charity drive or visit an orphanage with a friend. If you are talented at playing a musical instrument, take one along and a friend who can sing. Regular volunteer sessions to help those less fortunate than you are a primary distraction from feeling sorry for yourself.

Note: I chose the following activities to enjoy with my friend/partner. It helps me a great deal with managing my stress:

_____

_____

_____

_____

_____

_____

_____

_____

_____

_____

_____

Overthinking Time to Tame It

Overthinking and analyzing beyond normal parameters can ruin a relationship. Coupled with the fear of abandonment, heightened overanalyzing and incessant thinking in the negative create distress and discord within the boundaries of a relationship.

Overthinking is a far cry from just thinking; the former is disruptive and can become responsible for the loss of trust and commitment within a relationship.

Destructive Manifestations of Overthinking

What are they?

- Indulging in the luxury of mind reading. I say 'luxury' because you wrongly assume you know what the other person's thoughts are.

- Overthinking and overanalyzing results in the inevitable—paralysis of the mind and the inability to make a decision.

- Allowing catastrophic thoughts to take over. You think of the worst-case scenario. Or you place a past incident under the microscope and start to dissect and analyze every minute detail until you have made up enough "evidence" to build a complaint, start an argument or display negative emotions and behavior.

Rumination worry is the main factor that gives life to the above three factors. Consistent worry and dwelling on the problems eventually manifest into one giant ball of problems that slowly rolls over and squashes any chances you have of maintaining a relationship with friends, family, or a partner.

Your constant need to dissect and scrutinize the continuous "what ifs" is not limited to your mind frame; people close to you can feel it, and it makes them wary of a relationship with you.

So, how do you stop the constant worry?

First, you must call it out, accept and own your weakness—you are an overthinker. Go on, say it:

"I am an overthinker!"

There that's done. Now you own the weakness. And because you have named it and owned it, you have the power to break it, tame it, and frame it, thus ending its power over you. This next exercise will help you to do just that.

Exercise 48: Taming My Overthinking Habits

Trigger Example: Your partner says something to annoy you; they mention a past event that you found sensitive. You begin to overthink, and those few words uttered by your partner are turning into a problem that is going to start manifesting several other past incidents as well to create a full-blown crisis in your mind.

1. **Own it:** Stop the thought from snowballing into a huge problem, and realize you are overthinking. Tell yourself—"I am overthinking, and it's going to sabotage this day and this moment."

Now that you have called out the process let it settle in your mind. Give the process some time to properly manifest, all the while remaining conscious of the fact that you are overanalyzing. If it helps, take the time and give it a maximum of five minutes before you begin your 'fixing' process.

Exercise for later: What triggered the emotional avalanche?

_____

_____

_____

_____

_____

_____

2. **Distract:** Now that you have named and owned the thoughts, it's time to get rid of them.

- Distract your mind from its suspicious and over-analytical state to the present. Ask your partner a random question (about work, etc.) and let their voice distract you from the tumble of toxic thoughts in your head.

- Choose to change the scenery and move away from where you are. Perhaps get up and walk outside with your partner. Link arms and ask them how their day was. Make plans for the next day and ask them about going out and what they want to do.

- Remain conscious of the receding turmoil in your mind—you are telling yourself that you are not going to overanalyze that one statement and get upset. And gradually, that bubbly feeling of anger/sadness/annoyance that was threatening right beneath your calm composure starts to recede, and you have not reacted. You have not sabotaged yet another happy moment with your partner.

Document your experience

_____

_____

_____

_____

3. **Recognize the trigger taking place and halt the thought process:**

   "Oh no, that statement is triggering my analytical behavior. I don't want it to continue further." By doing so, you can become aware of triggers that lead to your over-analytical behavior and learn to avoid them.

4. **Fix it:** Recognizing, admitting, and owning your shortcomings is the first step to finding a solution to your disruptive thoughts. To do so, you must analyze and root out the triggers that start your overthinking mindset. Use your journal to analyze your behavior. Try to see how wrong it is and put yourself in the other person's position to try to understand what they said better. Quite often, you will realize you jumped to conclusions too quickly and ended up spoiling a perfectly good moment.

Document your experience

Exercise 49: What Are Your Triggers?

Recognize every time you go into rumination, analysis, paralysis mode, and STOP. Those are your triggers; understand what types of behavior or talk from the other person sets them off.

Think back to a pattern; every time your over-analytical behavior was triggered. What were the causes? Are they typical reasons?

I often get emotional and over-analytical when:

_____

_____

_____

_____

_____

_____

_____

_____

_____

_____

_____

_____

_____

_____

_____

Interpersonal Effectiveness for Solid Relationships

Relationships need to be nurtured; the more care and effort you put toward maintaining a relationship, the stronger it grows. And a deep-rooted relationship, like a big strong tree that has a network of deep roots, has the power to weather a few storms without falling down. That should be your goal in your relationship.

For people dealing with BPD establishing strong roots becomes more difficult than it is for the average person. You have so many hurdles to get through; emotional dysfunctions, over-analytical behavior, and rumination worry, to begin with.

To help you get over these hurdles through dialectical behavior therapy, special interpersonal skills have been developed as guidelines to help you keep your relationships within healthy parameters.

DBT Interpersonal Effectiveness Skills

1. FAST

2. GIVE

3. THINK

4. DEAR MAN

These skills are aimed at helping you to build and maintain your relationships effectively. The skills are simple and have been developed and fine-tuned from those of average individuals who enjoy successful relationships.

The following exercises are designed to help you overcome your attachment disorders that are responsible for abandonment issues and discord in your relationships.

1. FAST

This set of skills was developed to help you maintain self-respect within the boundaries of your relationship.

F = Fair

A = (n0) Apologies

S = Sticking to values

T = Truthful

These are the four skills that FAST is based on. Ideally, they should be practiced in sequence to get over a trigger. However, to begin with, you can practice one skill at a time until you master them all and can use FAST as a set of skills to overcome your emotional attachment dysfunctions and build on self-respect.

Exercise 50: Using FAIR Skills

FAIR teaches you to be fair in your thinking. It helps you to avoid your over-analytical, judgmental, and dramatic thinking patterns. Instead, you are thinking in a balanced context.

Think: How is the situation affecting them, and why are they responding thus? How is it affecting me and my emotions and behavior?

Avoid thoughts such as:

- "I am totally helpless." (don't make yourself out to be the victim).

- "They are behaving very selfishly!" (don't judge without knowing all the facts).

Balanced thinking works to help you understand the situation and avoid seeing yourself as a helpless victim, thus boosting your confidence.

Write: Today I practiced my FAIR skills by:

_____

_____

_____

_____

_____

In the end, I felt:

_____

_____

_____

Exercise 51: (no) Apologies

Apologize when the need calls for an apology. Remember, a relationship works on a give-and-take basis. Being FAIR and trying to understand a situation will help you gauge whether you need to apologize or not.

Since FAST is about boosting your self-image, you must learn the skill of not apologizing if the situation does not call for one. Avoid being the "giver" all the time and assert yourself. Do not apologize all the time because you want to avoid conflict and shy away from arguments. Every time you apologize unnecessarily, a seed of resentment grows deep within you and will eventually grow so much that it will kill the roots of your relationship tree. Therefore, recognize and STOP apologizing when the need does not call for one.

Write:

'Today, I was able to stand my ground. I didn't give in and apologized to maintain the peace. I explained my point of view, and I was successful. It did not sabotage my relationship because I was honest about my feelings and not trying to concede because of my fear of abandonment."

How did that act of not apologizing make you feel?

Has your relationship improved after?

Exercise 52: Sticking to Values

Safeguard and honor your values. They should not be mere statements but real actions performed by you. If you say you honor your parents, show them that you care by allocating enough time toward them. Sometimes you may consider yourself an honorable person, but you may not always act on those principles. Why is that? Indulge in some self-reflection to discover what your true values are, and then make sure you honor them.

What are my values, and how passionate am I about safeguarding them?

1. _____

_____

2. _____

_____

3. _____

_____

4. _____

_____

5. _____

_____

6. _____

_____

(Add more if needed)

Exercise 53: Being Truthful To Yourself

This exercise is about honesty to yourself and the other person. How critical are you of a situation How honest are you about your feelings?

- Do you give in and agree merely to maintain the peace?

- Do you silently disagree and despise?

- Are you putting the situation out of proportion—making a mountain out of a molehill?

Stop making compromises that are not a true reflection of who you are. Stop seeing the other person in a context that works for you. Be honest and weigh the pros and cons before you come to a solution or conclusion.

Write: *'Today I practiced being honest. My friend/partner/family member was surprised to see that side of me, but it felt good to know I was being true to myself. I did not feel the usual resentment after, and I felt more empowered and happier that my opinion was valued."*

When did you use the TRUTHFUL skill?

_____

_____

_____

_____

_____

_____

What was the outcome?

_____

_____

_____

_____

_____

How did you feel after?

_____

_____

_____

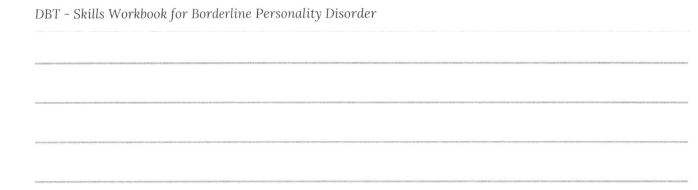

FAST will help you to become more assertive, avoid giving in and build self-worth. In turn, you will hold fewer grudges and feel less animosity toward the other person. Festering thoughts of resentment can grow and bubble over to cause a rift in a relationship. But practicing your FAST skills will help you to turn that around and enjoy an open, honest relationship.

2. GIVE

Use the GIVE skill to build a new relationship on successful communication and actions, and also to maintain an old relationship and breathe new life into the partnership. GIVE focuses on building a positive and respectful relationship dynamic.

G = Gentle

I = Interested

V = Validate

E = Easy manner

Exercise 54: GENTLE Skill

Instead of a full-on attack, practice a gentle approach to communicating with the other person. Jumping down their throat when you are in the height of emotional turmoil will only create discord, fear, disgust, and a rift in the relationship. Choose to communicate when you are both cooled down and are no longer aggressive. Show the other person you love and respect them instead of attacking them—despite your love for them, which sadly gets sidelined when you forget to be GENTLE.

Write: "Today, I felt my anger boil over because I was hurt. I usually attack to hide the hurt and my vulnerabilities. But this time, I closed my eyes and counted to ten. I waited for the emotional turmoil to settle and was successful in expressing myself gently."

The GENTLE skill helped me to successfully communicate today and see respect in the other person's eyes. I felt:

_____

_____

_____

_____

_____

_____

Exercise 55: Interested Skills

Further strengthen the respectful relationship bond by showing interest in what they are saying. Looking around, averting your eyes, and engaging in something else while they are talking is going to convey one message— *"I am not interested."*

When the other person is talking, show respect by holding their gaze. Look them in the eyes, and nod your head to acknowledge you are following the conversation. An occasional 'oh, I see,' or 'aha' will encourage them to continue. Reply through your facial expressions by showing surprise, anger, and so on in connection to what is being said. Actively participate in the conversation through body language and allow the other person to have their say uninterrupted.

Sometimes people need to unburden themselves, and finding a sympathetic ear is a huge relief. Your relationships must be based on that basis where you each have time for the other.

Write: *"Today I learned to listen; it felt good to know I am a trusted confidante, and I was able to understand so much about my partner/friend/etc. I find that actively listening and showing an interest in what the other person is doing or saying greatly improves my status with them."*

How did I feel after practicing my INTERESTED skills?

_____

_____

_____

_____

_____

_____

Exercise 56: Validate Skills

While showing interest in what the other person is saying, it is important to validate their feelings in a gesture of support. What you must do is follow the conversation and then reflect on the other person's emotional state through a statement.

If they are talking about losing out on their promotion at work, you can mirror their sentiments by saying: "It must have made you feel disappointed. I'm so sorry!"

Write about an incident where you were able to overcome your emotional shortcomings to actually listen and lend a sympathetic ear to someone else. Write about how you practiced your validation skills.

_____

_____

_____

_____

_____

Exercise 57: Easy Manner Skill

Enhance your GIVE skill by compounding all of the above skills in an easy and approachable manner. You can be gentle and interested and validate the other person's feelings in an approachable manner. Keep emotional outbursts in check. Do not overreact and discourage the other person from connecting with you. Even if what they are saying about themselves triggers your emotional dysfunctions, keep them in check and remain calm so the other person can continue interacting with you.

Write about a time you kept your emotions in check and let the other person unburden without feeling intimidated by outbursts from your end.

- How did it feel to practice restraint, remain calm, and project in an easy manner?

_____

_____

_____

3. THINK

This skill aims at stopping you from developing negative emotions toward others. The skill helps you to see the other person in a broader sense and not just a boxed opinion that you form from an emotional and biased point of view because of the hurt the other person caused you.

Thinking helps you to look at the other person in a fairer context by thinking about the pros and cons of their reaction from a wider perspective.

T = Think

H = Have empathy

I = Interpretation of the other person

N = Notice their behavior in a more positive light

K = Kindness which can be incorporated into your response

Exercises 58: THINK Skill

top what you are thinking as the situation is escalating and THINK about the other person. Try to see beyond the emotion you are dealing with and really look at the other person.

- Are they also just as angry as you are now, or could they be dealing with another less aggressive emotion, like sadness or bewilderment?

- Are they being unfair, or are they struggling to meet you in the middle?

- Try to place yourself in their position and think.

- Are they looking at you in the same unreasonable context that you are looking at them? Or do you see them struggling to meet you in the middle?

Take away the veil of emotion you are looking through to really THINK about the other person's reaction; it may not be the same as yours. That changes everything because what you thought about them before, the thought that made you despise them, *could* be blown out of proportion.

Write: Today, I got to practice my THINK skill.

"I was angry and automatically assumed ....was matching my mood. But when I stopped to think, I realized I was only assuming they were matching my mood when in fact .... was struggling to overcome the hurt/sadness/bewilderment they were feeling. The moment I realized that fact, my emotional response changed, and I felt.

Exercise 59: Have Empathy Skill

Stop riding on your emotional response, no matter how hurt or angry you feel, and for minute, switch sides. Get out of your emotional turmoil and try to be sympathetic in your judgment of the other person's behavior.

Think with empathy:

- What if you were the other person?

- You are standing there looking at them, assuming what their emotional response is based on but what happens when you switch sides?

↓

- Flip the perspective become the other person, and look at yourself from their position? Are they angry, or are they really scared and confused?

↓

- Allow yourself empathy so you can feel compassion for them even if you are angry. What are they going through emotionally right now? Sadness perhaps and not anger?

↓

- For a moment, don't think of yourself as the victim but try to feel sorry for the other person. It may not be an easy skill to master, but when you try to switch sides, the action suddenly makes you more aware that the other person may be just as vulnerable as you.

Today I practiced HAVE EMPATHY skills, and it helped me to be more compassionate in my thinking. Therefore, I saw .... in a different light. Being kinder toward them, even when I am really angry or sad at their behavior, has helped me to evolve and feel less like a victim. When I don't feel like a victim, I don't react in self-defense. Instead, I feel:

Exercise 60: Interpretation Skills

Once you learn to develop empathy for the other person, you can learn to change your interpretations of them.

Do you often interpret the other person in haste from your emotional perspective? Their reactions could be based on a whole different angle than your initial thoughts. Sometimes it takes us a few minutes and a tumble of thoughts to realize why the other person is behaving the way they do:

Thought 1.

> "She is being mean and unreasonable and is arguing with me today because she is used to having her own way and taking what she wants."

↓

Thought 2.

> "She is so used to having her own way. That may be why she doesn't realize she can be unreasonable and mean at times."

↓

Thought 3.

> "Maybe she had a bad day and is feeling depressed; that's why she is overreacting and being mean."

↓

> "She looks tired and harassed; maybe she has been pushed around all day and has had enough of being taken advantage of and is reacting meanly because she has been treated that way all day. Maybe she needs some kindness to be shown to her."

Can you see how your interpretation of a person changes the way you see them? Once you change your interpretation of them, your emotional response may suddenly go from anger to sympathy. They then become a victim of sorts, and you become their salvation.

So, instead of becoming your enemy, they become your "friend in need," and that is a whole boost of encouragement for you.

Today I practiced my Interpretation skills:

_____

_____

_____

_____

I don't feel like a victim when I do so because:

_____

_____

_____

_____

Exercise 61: Notice Skills

Try to take notice of the other person's reactions to you. So, you had an argument and walked away; you felt anger and resentment. The next day you see them, and those same emotions start bubbling up, but if you make an effort to look at them, you just may notice a smile. Did they smile at you? What could that mean?

Look again:

- They are smiling and looking nervous.

- Are they reaching out to you?

- Maybe they want to patch things up?

- Maybe they are not angry with you?

Often when we make an effort to take notice of the other person, we are angry/disappointed, etc., as we realize they are not carrying the grudge the same way we assume they are. If you don't look, you don't see. And there is a lot you could be missing out on by not looking.

Did you practice your notice skills? What were your observations? Did it change your relationship with someone?

Exercise 62: Kindness Skill

It is not easy to forgive someone who hurt us immediately. It takes time. But on your part, your response can be kind.

Instead of:
"You always say things to hurt me! I hate you!"
You can try:
"What you said was very hurtful, and I need some time to myself to get over it, but I hope we can stop hurting each other this way in the future."

Showing kindness prevents the relationship from being based on verbal abuse, yelling negative statements at each other, and escalating the hurt. Responding kindly makes the other person realize they were being mean and hurt you because you did not try to hurt them back, although *your* feelings were hurt.

What are your thoughts on reacting kindly? Were there situations you could have handled differently?

_____

_____

_____

_____

_____

_____

_____

_____

_____

4. DEAR MAN

In order to strengthen and maintain a relationship, you have to learn to be tactful; the DEAR MAN skill has been designed to help you to try and get what you want out of a relationship by doing just that. You may or may not get what you want every time, but it will help maintain a pleasant atmosphere within the relationship. And help you to describe your needs in a cordial and non-conflictive way.

Exercise 63: DEAR MAN Skill

Unlike the previous skills, DEAR MAN skills must be used in combination toward a successful goal. Each skill works in sequence to help you

D = **Describe.** Be clear and explain your needs. My office has planned a workshop over the weekend, which they say is compulsory to attend if we want to apply for promotions.

E = **Express.** The workshop is designed to help us improve, plus I really want to fit in and be a team player.

A = **Assert.** I feel the workshop will help me to learn more, and I feel I have a very good chance of getting promoted and enjoying a salary increase.

R = **Reinforce.** Next weekend, let's plan a vacation for us to spend time together.

M = **Mindful.** Be in the moment and alert. Do not let your mind wander to what your boss will say if you can't go. Concentrate on what you are doing now—expressing your need to go to the workshop.

A = **Appear Confident.** Are you scared about telling your partner you need to be away from them with office colleagues for a weekend? Don't show it; it may put your intentions into question. Instead, be confident and focused on why you are going; to improve and have an equal opportunity of getting promoted.

N = **Negotiate.** Change tactics when you feel you are not going to get a positive response. The workshop is booked at a hotel. You could book a private stay, and we could spend time together when I am not in the training sessions, or why don't you plan a vacation with your buds while I'm away? That way you won't be bored without me.

Today I used the DEAR MAN skill to explain myself and achieve a need. This is what happened.

_____

_____

_____

_____

_____

_____

_____

_____

The experience and results were different from other times because:

_____

_____

_____

_____

_____

_____

_____

_____

_____

When Your Relationship Needs Emotional Regulation

Emotional dysfunctions are nothing new when dealing with BPD, still, it does not make it easy.

A typical example would be your anticipation of the weekend. You have worked hard all week and have planned a nice, relaxed Saturday with your family. You plan to savor Friday as the prelude, a movie, a good dinner, and fun.

Friday morning rolls around; it's easier than the week has been because of the reward of rest the next day. But as evening draws near, that bubble of excitement seems to have popped, and your mood is down as though something is wrong—what? It's even worse because you feel deflated but can't quite put a specific reason or emotion to that mood. Friday evening is spoilt, as you feel totally drained now, and it does not create the climax to the weekend you hoped to enjoy, yet you don't know why, as defeated and dealing with a headache, you go to bed early.

This activity will help you control such erratic mood swings—learn to name them and tame them!

Learn to control which emotions affect you instead of rolling along from one to the other it's exhaustive and a damper to your plans.

Exercise 64: Worksheet for Recognizing and Dealing With Your Emotions

Emotions can be categorized as positive and negative.

Negative Emotions	Positive Emotions
Respected	Lonely
Loved	Frustrated
Bubbly	Nervous
Excited	Envious
Satisfied	Hopeless

Happy	Bored
Pleased	Insecure
Respected	Exhausted
Proud	Scared
Determined	Guilty
Secure	Angry
Content	Sad
Smart	Shy

1. Pick an emotion and use this worksheet to dissect it and understand the connection you have with it. Try choosing an emotion you are dealing with at the moment. Or try to think back to the most recent emotional dysfunction you experienced.

Perhaps your friends met up over the weekend, and even though you insisted you were busy and could not join, you resented them meeting without you. What did you feel? Angry, lonely, sad? Recall those feelings and identify the specific emotion.

Here, I have used loneliness as the emotion for the example.

1. Choose an Emotion (preferably one you experience often)	1. The emotion I choose is: **LONELINESS**
2. What does that emotion look like to you?	2. Draw the emotions/doodles/words, etc.
3. What action do you commonly associate with this emotion	3. • I feel let down by my friends and avoid their calls. • I stay isolated and avoid socializing
4. How intense is your emotion on a scale of 1–10	9
5. Write about your feelings and thoughts connected to the emotion	My friends were quick to meet without me; I am always left out. They could have canceled the meet-up.

How Can This Exercise Help Me?

1. Can I feel better after this exercise; will it help me?

Yes, if you take the example of the emotion, loneliness, and weigh it against the action that caused it, what do you really think?

You were busy and could not join, but you were asked. Also, you did not choose to ask them to reschedule. Perhaps if you had, they would have. Feeling sorry for yourself and 'lonely' was therefore almost voluntary and uncompounded. You were not excluded, and loneliness should have no direct impact on you.

It is just an emotion you would naturally feel, but not to be dwelled upon and base your actions on—choosing isolation and avoidance. You took that emotion too far because you indulged your feeling of loneliness instead of naming and taming.

2. Can such a simple worksheet help me?

It's the simplest form of a solution that helps us the most. The thoughts you put down in the worksheet help you to reflect, analyze and change your perspective of how you deal with an emotion.

Understand the intensity through which the emotion grips you by drawing. Let your feelings flow through to the paper. A mess of scratchy lines to show how anger grips you will tell you how intensely you embrace that emotion—next time, let go and step back. Use the THINK skill to practice empathy and control over your emotions.

Exercise 65: Active Listening and Communications Skills Workbook

Active listening opens up a healthy communication channel within a relationship. Giving each party a chance to have an equal share in the conversation.

This worksheet exercise works on the following factors:

*   communication; verbally and non-verbally
*   equal exchange of thoughts, emotions, and ideals
*   a chance to reflect

Active Listening Skills

Practice your active listening skills by creating sample conversations and responses to help you understand how to use each skill.

Active Listening the 8 Steps: How to follow them and sample questions	My Examples: Add your own example conversations in these columns following the same parameters outlined in the eight steps of Active Listening
Ask Open-ended Questions: Ask questions that allow the other person to contribute to the conversation: "Don't you think the speech given by Mary today was too long? Which parts do you think she could have left out?"	
Request Clarification: If you don't understand, don't feel bad asking: Avoid being rude, don't say, "you were talking so fast I understood nothing!" Instead, you can say, "can you explain that once more, I'm sorry it was not very clear to me."	
Be Attentive: Use body language to show you are listening. Nod your head and ask occasional pointed questions: "Oh, okay, so then what did you do?"	
Summarize: If you have been narrating a long story, stop and recap, helping the other person keep up. Or, if you are listening to a long story, repeat what you just heard:	

"Okay, so let me get this right, you found out you didn't get the promotion because your colleague decided to take sole credit for the project you both worked on in March?"	
Paraphrase: You can paraphrase to confirm what you just said. Do not try to change the objective of what the other person was saying. Don't say, "I think you meant to say that…." Instead, say, "Oh, so you think……." If you feel the expression was a bit too much, you can give the person the opportunity to change what they just said by paraphrasing. "Let me get this right: so you are saying that so and so should not…?"	
Reflect Feelings: Show your support by reflecting on the emotions the other person is expressing: Look angry for parts of the conversation that involve a conflict the other person is dealing with. Look sad if they are talking about an emotional difficulty, and so on.	
Be Attuned to Feelings: Form a connection with the person during the conversation. This involves recognizing the emotional state of the other person to engage and connect with	

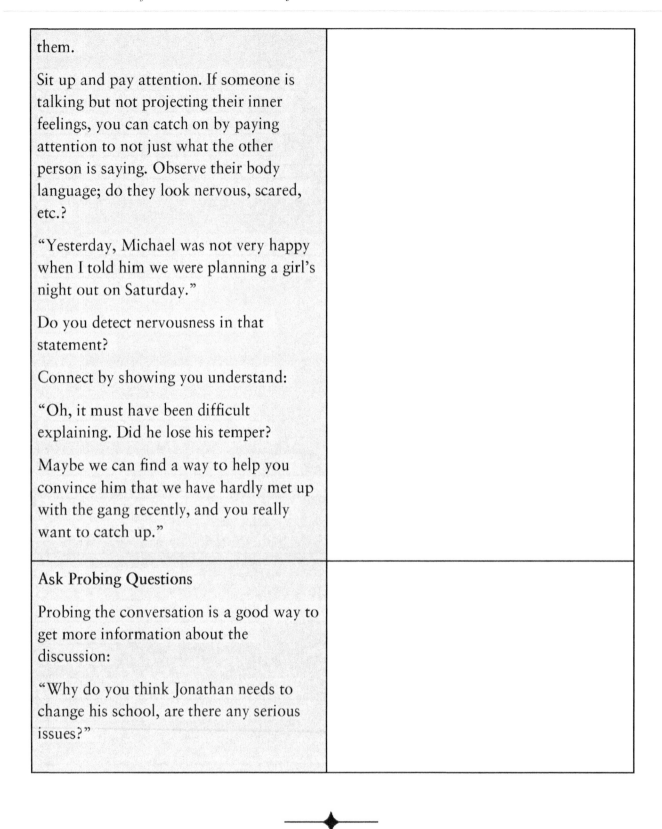

them.

Sit up and pay attention. If someone is talking but not projecting their inner feelings, you can catch on by paying attention to not just what the other person is saying. Observe their body language; do they look nervous, scared, etc.?

"Yesterday, Michael was not very happy when I told him we were planning a girl's night out on Saturday."

Do you detect nervousness in that statement?

Connect by showing you understand:

"Oh, it must have been difficult explaining. Did he lose his temper?

Maybe we can find a way to help you convince him that we have hardly met up with the gang recently, and you really want to catch up."

Ask Probing Questions

Probing the conversation is a good way to get more information about the discussion:

"Why do you think Jonathan needs to change his school, are there any serious issues?"

Radical Acceptance Skills

Learn how to take control of your intense emotions to stop reacting in a negative and highly disruptive manner. The goal is to identify, consider, and finally understand the negative emotion. We cannot control everything; therefore, it is wise to understand what's within and what's beyond your control. By gracefully accepting the latter and being mindful, you can reign in that emotion and stop it from causing damage. The goal is to do this without changing the situation but merely accepting it.

Acceptance of the other person's behavior is important as a factor you can't change. You can change your behavior and reactions; in this case, accepting the other for who they are and not retaliating is the control you wield over yourself.

Exercise 66: Radical Acceptance Skills Worksheet

This worksheet comprises five sections, answering each question after careful deliberation. The moment you make a discovery about your reactions and triggers, log that in.

Recall a particularly disturbing situation you experience and answer the question. The more recent, the better.

1. Write about the situation that is causing you distress and pain.

    Try to identify the trigger and the chain of events that led to it. What happened? And how did you react? Who was involved?

2. How did everyone involved in the situation behave? What did you do? And how much did your behavior influence the situation?

_____

_____

_____

_____

_____

_____

_____

_____

_____

_____

3. Were there others involved in the incident and how did they behave? How much did their behavior influence the situation?

_____

_____

_____

_____

_____

_____

_____

_____

_____

_____

_____

_____

4. As events unfolded, did you have control over any part of the situation? What could you control? And what were the occurrences and behavior you could not control?

_____

_____

_____

_____

_____

_____

_____

5. Describe in detail and, after careful deliberation, your reaction to the entire event.

When answering this question, keep in mind that a reaction takes place when you allow your emotions to take control of your behavior, but a response is the result of deliberate behavior. Based on that theory, what was your reaction to the situation? How did the situation affect you emotionally?

_____

_____

_____

_____

_____

_____

_____

_____

_____

_____

_____

_____

_____

Now that we have run through several skills, theories, and exercises that validate the need for special attention and some allowance when you are dealing with BPD, it is also important to understand that a diagnosis of BPD does not necessarily make you immune to disruptive, rude and unsympathetic behavior.

Let's take Hilary, our subject at the start of this chapter. Her behavior, which caused her relationships to end, was due to her condition—dealing with BPD. But do you think that Hilary's treatment of her partners would have been justified if, at that point, she knew about her condition?

No!

Being diagnosed with BPD does not mean the other person, whether a friend, lover, or family member, has to concede to your disruptive behavior. While better understanding will certainly make more sense within the structure of the relationship, practicing patience, restraint, and acceptance on your part will have the greatest influence on the relationship. A BPD diagnosis is not a free pass to give in to your negative emotions.

With that settled, we must tackle another conundrum—what if the person diagnosed with BPD feels they are not deserving of a healthy and happy relationship?

Someone with low self-esteem who has lost all hope and denies themselves happiness cannot find fulfillment inside of a relationship; they are so lost in their own hopelessness they no longer recognize the person they have become.

What, then, is the solution? Is there hope? Yes! It's time to get to know the stranger in the mirror!

Chapter THREE

When You are Looking At a Stranger in the Mirror

As I began to love myself, I found that anguish and emotional suffering were only warning signs that I was living against my own truth.

– Charlie Chaplin

Sometimes we look in the mirror and we dislike our close-set eyes, our too-big nose, or the way our hair stands up. But what if you look in the mirror and you see an enemy, a loathsome creature staring back at you?

What do you do, and how do you rescue yourself and bring back a recognizable you to gaze back from the mirror?

You start to take a good long look at the person in the mirror until you slowly start to recognize some features. You begin to reframe your mind, and as you do, you notice a transformation taking place. That unrecognizable thing is starting to look familiar. You are no longer struggling with feelings of shame or disgust at the kind of person you think you are. Your self-esteem is growing!

What I described are common traits a person with BPD deals with; a lack of self-esteem, the constant desire to look down on themselves, and regarding who they are with contempt and disgust.

The skills we are going to discuss in this chapter will help you to slowly reframe your mind and bring back the person you once were. And become accepting of healthy relationships that can boost your recovery.

Mindfulness Practices for Building Self—Esteem

The use of positive affirmations can help to replace negative and wrong self-images with accurate and positive ones. You can do so by retraining your brain and changing the beliefs you hold about yourself.

Change negative to positive by giving yourself support and encouragement emotionall through affirmations. In exercise 2, we learned the use of affirmations for building self-esteem a a self-help therapy. Now let's look at more such statements that can help you to heal and chang your negative self-image.

Exercise 67: Affirmations to Build Self-Image

Practice repeating the affirmations at a time that is suitable for you.

- early morning

- at the end of the day

- as you enter your daily thoughts in your journal

- you could have a collection of affirmations written on a card to help you get through the da

- repeat them several times throughout the day and choose the ones that resonate the most

My Daily Affirmations

- I am not who I have diagnosed myself to be.
- I am worth it.
- I can heal; it is possible.
- There are so many positives in my life.
- It's okay to have bad days.
- I am strong, and I can endure bad days.
- I accept my mental health challenges, and I am not ashamed of my struggles.
- I will soon start to feel better about things.
- I am worthy of being loved and I love myself.
- I am not weak; I am stronger than I think.
- My feelings and thoughts matter.
- I am accepting of myself just the way I am.
- I am happy with myself.
- I feel safe.

Add more of your own:

_____

_____

_____

_____

_____

_____

Exercise 68: Body Scan Meditation

Body scan meditation is typically done to help people locate their pain points. But this time, you will learn to scan your body to find ways to appreciate and love yourself without being judgmental. Connect with the sensations you discover as you concentrate and focus on your body. By fine-tuning your sensory experiences, you grow to love and accept yourself for who you are.

Step 1: Find a Quiet Place Where You Will Not Be Disturbed

- Lie down with your arms at your sides. Or sit comfortably with your arms folded in your lap or by your side. Just get comfortable, that's what counts.

- Close your eyes and deep breathe a few times.

- Scan your body by becoming aware of each part; linger over each section, scanning for any sensations you may be feeling. Do you detect any stress?

- Become more conscious of your breathing. Focus on inhaling, the air passing through your nostrils and filling your belly, then exhale and feel that whoosh of air leaves your body. Be in the moment and concentrate on your breathing.

- Your mind may wander on and off, and that's okay. Don't dwell on those other thoughts get back to concentrating on your breathing.

- Now, become conscious of your feet and wriggle your toes. What do you feel? A coolness the soft touch of the surface your feet are on. Are they sweaty? Can you relax them, starting with your feet? Continue to inhale and exhale.

- Move your focus to your legs. Start from the ankle up; are they tense? Painful? Breathe in and out. Now relax your legs, moving up to your thighs. How do they feel? Accept them for the way they are and relax. Try to envision the tightness slipping away.

- Move over your body to your stomach, and feel it rise and fall with every breath. Do you feel anxiety there? Butterflies, nervousness, an uneasy feeling? Accept them. And feel those sensations as they wash over you; no need to try and change them. Accept those feelings Keep breathing in and out.

- Focus on your stomach rising and falling. Feel as though you are sinking deep into yourself with every exhale. If you are lying down, feel as though you're going deeper into the mattress. If you can't envision that it's okay, concentrate on your breathing.

- Once you feel acceptance in your stomach of the fullness, the sensations move to your chest

- Become conscious of your chest rising and falling as you breathe. Concentrate, breathe in and out. Can you feel your heartbeat? Can you feel the endless rhythm?

- Celebrate your beating heart and be thankful for its tireless work pumping oxygen through your body. Appreciate being alive.

- Breathe in and move your focus to your back. This is where you will feel the most tension. Is there a tightness? Can you relax your shoulders? Feel as though you are carrying a heavy burden and just put it down. Feel the pleasure of ridding yourself of all that weight. Smile; you feel more relaxed. Breathe in and out.

- Let go of wandering thoughts entering your mind. Concentrate on breathing in and out.

- Now move your attention to your face. Do your eyes feel tired? Are they throbbing? Can you feel your nostrils flare as you breathe? Relax your lips, were they clamped down tightly? Smile, and as you do, feel the muscles in your cheeks move.

- Imagine your face smiling at you and smiling back. Appreciate the person you are.

- Continue to breathe in and out for another three minutes. Move your head from side to side. Now open your eyes. As you get up, be conscious of every part of your body helping with the action.

- Appreciate your body.

My Thoughts After I Performed a Body Scan:

I realize my body works hard to keep me alive, and I appreciate it. I know I must take better care of my body. To do so, I must: (write about the type of diet changes, physically gratifying activities, and emotional upliftment exercises and activities that can help)

_____

_____

_____

_____

_____

_____

_____

_____

_____

_____

◆

Self-Appraisal to Appreciate Who You Are

Your appraisal of yourself is based on your negative and positive opinions of who you ar When dealing with BPD, you often tend to be overly critical of yourselves, depriving yourselves love and appreciation. You tend to judge yourselves harshly and unkindly based on your person opinions.

This exercise will help you identify those personal beliefs to manage a change and cultivate more appreciative overview of yourself. Change how you appraise yourself and how you vie yourself through your behavior and beliefs.

Answer the following questions leisurely; do not be in a hurry. Reflect on each question ar think deeply before you answer.

Exercise 69: Self-Appraisal Worksheet

	My Answers
Q1. What do you love most about yourself?	
Q2. What objectives can I achieve the most successfully?	
Q3. How do I react to criticism?	
Q4. What are the achievements that I can be proud of?	
Q5. What's my reaction to a positive comment someone gives me?	
Q6. If I am criticized, or I make a mistake, what do I do? How do I feel?	
Q7. If given the choice to make a change in your life, what would it be? Is there an ambition you would want to fulfill right now?	

Q8. Name your talents or positive factors about yourself.	
9. At what times do you feel good about who you are, and what are the contributing factors?	
10. In what moments do you really feel appreciative of who you are, the times you can accept and be comfortable with yourself?	

Evaluate your answers to discover your true self.

1. How did you feel when filling in the answers?

2. What self-truths and revelations about yourself did you make?

3. What do you feel you discovered in each answer?

_____

_____

_____

_____

_____

_____

_____

4. Can you identify any negative thoughts about yourself that you feel you can change to turn around your harsh perception of yourself?

_____

_____

_____

_____

_____

———————◆———————

Coping With Distress Caused by Low Self-Image

There are times you can be your worst enemy and critic. The result is a low self-image that attacks you even more violently than outsider remarks. Everyone experiences low self-esteem from time to time, and even the most confident people can feel like a failure. Experiencing and letting go of those inhibitions is the healthy option before they grow and fester; do so by taking time to reflect on your positive character strengths.

Therefore, this exercise focuses on helping you to recall past moments when you were at your best.

Exercise 70: Me At My Best Worksheet

Step 1: Recall

Think back to an event when you were at your best. A time you accomplished something to be proud of, a particularly difficult problem you were able to overcome in time. A time when your efforts yielded positive results that made you feel invigorated, accomplished, overjoyed, and proud.

Take your time to recall the incident in as much detail as possible.

Step 2: Story Time

Prepare to write your story. Begin by jotting down the details; what happened, the cause, the problem that evolved, your reaction, your actions, and the final outcome.

Make it as vivid as possible and include the feelings and emotions you associate with every phase of the story. Recount in detail how the events unfolded and how you reacted. Take a moment to close your eyes and recall the event. Pay attention to the minute details your mind dredges up. Then write down the events you remember.

_____

_____

_____

_____

_____

_____

_____

_____

_____

_____

_____

_____

_____

_____

_____

_____

_____

Step 3: Structure

Structure your story; take the notes you just made and divide them up to form the beginning, the middle, and the very impactful ending. Then write your story.

My Story

Step 4: Read Your Story and Analyze

Read your story over again, and highlight and circle sections and words that focus on how strong you were. Reflect on your positive characteristics, and recall them to overshadow the negatives you have been harboring.

Write them here as a sentence of one descriptive word/line.

E.g., I can face challenges and overcome them when I try = I am STRONG

My Strengths, Positive Characteristics, and Talents

_____

_____

_____

_____

_____

_____

Relook at yourself and establish a new perception of who you are. Use this story to uplift yourself every time you feel discouraged or tend to sell yourself short.

Exercise 71: Self-Esteem Sentence Stems

Use these sentence stems in conjunction with the strengths, talents, and positive self-images you discovered through your story. Choose a set of five questions from the list given below and answer them repeatedly for four to five weeks. In doing so, you will see how your answers change for the same question. That is an indication of your growing positivity as you explore your feelings, thoughts, and emotions in depth to come to some very important truths about yourself.

Self-esteem stem sentences:

- My strength comes from…

- I shine and grow when…

- It is difficult for me to admit…

- My life's dream is…

- What I love the most about myself is…

- I felt great when…

- What I most fear is…

- I do this secretly…

- This is what I desire the most…

- The one person I need in my life is…

- This week I plan to enjoy…

- It is difficult for me to…

Choose Your Questions and Use the Grid to Keep Track of Your Answers

Stem Question	Answer Week 1	Answer Week 2	Answer Week 3	Answer Week 4	Answer Week 5	My Observations
1.						
2.						
3.						
4.						
5.						

Automatic Negative Thoughts—ANTs

What if you had an 'off-switch' to turn off those toxic negative thoughts that crop up from time to time? The voices that keep up a string of negative chatter that you simply can't tune out of. You can't because they are automatic negative thoughts annoying little ANTs. Those little niggling ideas that pop into your head to say you can't, are not good enough, will never, and so on.

Did you know that out of the estimated 70,000 random thoughts a person has in one day, a large percentage are negative? This happens because you are more prone to thinking pessimistically. Sadly, those thoughts are capable of negatively influencing your emotions and behavior unless you take countermeasures.

The following exercise is designed to make you an ANTs exterminator. Use the following prompts to turn off or drown out the flow of automatic negative thoughts by challenging their authenticity and true depth.

Exercise 72: Turning Off the Flow of Negative Mental Chatter

Use these prompts to crush ANTs whenever they start seeping into your mind.

- What I am thinking right now is not true because…

- There has to be a different way to look at this. I think a more accurate account is…

- This problem is not impossible to solve. I can do the following to find a solution…

- Instead of giving up, what can I do to resolve this right now?

- Even if things spiral out of control, I will still be okay because I can…

- If I take these actions, I can find a solution…

My Notes: Today, I used the following prompts to crush my ANTs. It helped me to:

_____

_____

_____

_____

_____

Assertive Communication

This DBT skill helps you to find a balance in your communication with others that is not overly aggressive or too passive. When you adopt an assertive form of communication, you can successfully voice your thoughts coming across as being truthful and direct.

This happens because assertive communication is a form of acceptance; being responsible for your own actions instead of trying to pass the blame.

Use the chart below to assess where you stand in your communication style.

Aggressive	Assertive	Passive
forceful and aggressive	assertive but polite	easily giving in and being accommodating
talking in a raised voice	talking clearly and in a pleasant conversational form	talking very softly or mumbling
threatening or bullying behavior toward others	standing up for yourself when needed	easily pushed around by others
talking down	talk to others in an encouraging manner to help them feel positive about themselves	too modest and quickly downplays your accomplishments
forcing your beliefs and not considering those of others	find a compromise	easily complies to other people's requests
being too frank to the point of hurting the other person	be appropriately honest but within limits	hides true fact so as not to hurt the other person
glaring or trying to stare down the person you are talking to	maintain a friendly eye contact	avoids eye contact and tends to look away

Exercise 73: Practice scenarios

Use the given worksheet to practice assertive responses. An example is given for the first scenario. Make up three more and practice your assertive answers.

1. Scenario Judy called me and wanted to know if I could cover her shift next Sunday as a huge favor. I responded, *"Ordinarily, it would be no problem at all, but I have already made plans to spend Sunday with my kids, and I really don't want to disappoint them. I hope you understand."*
How I felt emotionally: I was happy that I didn't lie, I was straightforward, and I felt relieved I had cleared up the issue without feeling bad and having to disappoint my kids.
2. Scenario
How I felt emotionally:
3. Scenario
How I felt emotionally:

The Looking-Glass Self

Charles Horton Cooley has proposed a theory that an individual will develop a notion of themselves by observing how others perceive them. He calls it the looking-glass self. Social interactions they make represent a mirror through which they view their sense of self; measuring their values, worth and behavior.

In short, we are defined through the eyes of society and how they judge us. This concept has more weight with social media becoming an integral part of our society; the birth of the cyber self has taken place with artists seeking self-validation through Pinterest, a professional on LinkedIn, social butterflies on Instagram, and so on. The cyber self is constantly exposed to criticism and judgment.

Exercise 74: Changing the Looking-Glass Self

Scene 1:

How many incidents can you recall that base your sense of worth on the looking-glass self theory?

Choose one and write about it. Go into detail about the events and the criticism and judgments that eventually shaped your sense of self.

Scene 2: Flip it Around

Now, take this scenario and change the outcome, the verdict given by society. For example Let's say in your original event, you presented a painting you worked on very hard via a digita platform. You got some likes and a few words of encouragement. But not hundreds of likes o comments that made you feel highly talented. Were you motivated to continue painting more, o did you shift your interests elsewhere?

Now imagine an alternate response to your painting. Hundreds of likes, shares, and word of encouragement, and congratulations on your wonderful talent. What have you done? Gone o to paint more? Expanded into different mediums of creativity? Thought of yourself as a talente artist?

Can you see how your sense of self changed when society told you who you were?

What are your thoughts? Do you really need that type of validation, or can you find you own sense of worth and validation?

Stop Self-Sabotage

Self-sabotage takes place when you base your behavior, emotions, and thoughts on a series of events—triggers. They lead to self-destructive behavior by giving you an excuse to quit, avoid and give up.

Exercise 75: Identify Your Common Self-Sabotaging Triggers

Identify With Your Trigger Types

Scenario	Relatable Yes/No
1. You started a new fitness regime. You were hitting the gym daily and doing great. Then you came down with the flu. You recovered in two days, but you feel that maybe hitting the gym daily caused you to get sick, so you give up. 2. You started an online course for painting and enjoyed the activity. But when asked for their opinion, your friend gave you a critical review, so you decide you don't really have a talent for painting and decide to give up. 3. You work over the weekend preparing for an important pitch, but your boss finds a few details missing and points them out. You start to panic, berating yourself for missing out on vital information, and you fear you are not fit enough to make the presentation and that everyone sees you as a failure.	
1. You start working at your dream job, and you don't want to slack, so you put in extra hours, and everyone is pleased. But you fear if you stick to regular work hours, they may think you are slowing down. So, you go to work on weekends, too, until you end up tired and cranky all the time. 2. Your friends have signed up for yoga, and talk about how great it is for finding your center. You dislike yoga, but you join anyway because you think this is	

the best option to find your inner peace, which everyone is talking about. 3. Your friends want to plan a movie night, but you have to work late, and you insist they go without you. But after they do, you are angry because you feel they should have insisted on waiting for you and not gone at all.	
1. You finally publish your book. There are several good reviews, and you feel proud, but one speaks about a lack of depth and maybe improving on your content. You are devastated and feel like a failure because you got that one bad review. 2. You join a hiking group and enjoy the adventures, but you are always the last one tagging behind. Without waiting to improve, you quit, thinking you will never improve. 3. You go out on a date with someone you met at your kids' school and enjoy their company. Turns out they are vegan. So, you end the date thinking of never calling them again. You think it may be too much of a hassle to date someone with special preferences.	

My Reflections: What are your thoughts on the triggers you identify with? Can you avoid them? How?

_____

_____

_____

_____

Load Up On Your Emotional Regulation Skills

The ABC PLEASE skill is used to help you increase your positive outlook and experiences. By doing so, you can decrease vulnerabilities that are prone within an emotionally dysfunctional mind.

Exercise 76: ABC PLEASE skills

A: Accumulating Accumulate as many happy and positive experiences as you can. It's okay to layer the day with them. E.g.: cuddling with your four-legged friend or planning a road trip with friends. Your plans can be based on short-term (things you can experience in the present) and long-term; future plans for establishing a fulfilling life.	What positive short and long-term experiences can I add today?
B: Building Be assertive about all the good things you did. Plan more to build your confidence. Effective events that shape you and give your self-confidence a boost.	What are my plans for "building" my life?
C: Cope Prepare yourself to face a difficult situation. You know the scenario is inevitable, don't wait to improvise. Be fully prepared to deal with judgment, criticism, emotions, and behavior.	What are my strongest coping mechanisms?

PL: Treat Physical Illness Do not neglect your physical needs; rest when needed and keep to your scheduled doctors' appointments.	My treatment goals
A: Avoid Mood Altering Drugs Don't become dependent on drugs to design your mood. You can develop emotional self-regulation through exercises and determination. Drugs work only part of the time, and developing a dependency is another form of weakness.	What can I do to develop emotional self-regulation:
S: Balance Sleep Getting adequate sleep is crucial for being mentally and physically fit and strong. Late nights and long days lead to fatigue which gives way to easily falling victim to triggers and developing dependency weaknesses.	My new sleep schedule includes at least seven hours of sleep per night is:
E: Exercise Just 30 minutes a day will show you an improvement in emotional regulation, self-esteem, and confidence. Exercises to adopt • Aerobics and weight training to increase heart rate and release endorphins.	My personal exercise regime:

<ul><li>Boxercise.</li><li>Orienteering exercises are great for building confidence not just in the outdoors but within yourself. Here are some examples to try.<ul><li>three-leg compass walk</li><li>geocaching</li><li>closed course</li></ul></li></ul>	

Start small with baby steps. There is no rush, practice makes perfect, and with time you will soon start to see remarkable improvements. Self-image must be built gradually, do not liken it to your mood swings happening suddenly. Wait for the gradual improvement and you will find success.

On that note, let's explore changing moods and how fast they manifest and disappear.

Chapter FOUR

Coping With Moods That Change Faster Than You Can Tell

For a moment I felt joyful, and then I felt completely exhausted.

- Ottessa Moshfegh

Living with sudden and erratic mood changes is no walk in the park. One minute you are laughing with everyone else, and the next, you feel as though the walls are closing in on you and a feeling of dread takes over. People on the outside cannot fathom these sudden emotional changes, which makes it all the more difficult to cope with.

This chapter aims to help you reign in those runaway moods, to help you cope to control happiness, changing into sudden anger and excitement, and dying with feelings of despair. Let's look at conquering those sudden mood shifts that disappear as fast as they appear, as well as mood swings that can last for much longer and influence your emotions and behavior.

Being Mindful About Moods

Exercise 77: Mood Meter

Learn to be in touch with your moods and understand their range. The mood chart is a good guide for judging the intensity of your shifting moods. Use it to identify and add your moods and maintain a record of how intensely they shift across the grid.

*Add your mood to the appropriate section depending on how that mood makes you feel.

Mood Meter

Angry	Stressed	Enraged	Jittery	Shocked	H		Happy	Exhilarated	Motivated		
					I						
					G						
					H						
					E						
					N						
					E						
					R						
					G						
					Y						

UNPLEASANT ↑   →   ↓ **PLEASANT**

					L						
					O						
					W						
Disgusted	despair	Lonely	Tired	Sad			Serene	Cozy	Sleepy	Comfy	Restful
					E						
					N						
					E						
					R						
					G						
					Y						

- Do you see a pattern in how your moods shift?

E.g.: low energy to pleasant.

- What are the common types of moods you find yourself dealing with most often?

.g.: Low energy moods that often follow a high energy mood; I feel exhilarated one moment and ompletely drained the next.

_____

_____

_____

_____

_____

_____

_____

_____

Exercise 78: De-Stress With Mindful Walking

Deal with your heightened emotions by practicing mindful walking which can help to slow down the heart rate, reduce blood pressure, and the secretion of stress hormones.

Choose a path (outdoors is best) for a walk. A short ten-minute walk will do. What you are going to learn is mindful walking which is to become conscious of your surroundings and every step you take.

There is no destination to reach; simply walk. Be conscious of placing one step after the other, your surroundings, and nothing else.

1. Stand at the start of your path and deep breathe. Focus on your body and how you feel.

2. Begin to walk, conscious of how your body is moving with every step.

3. Be mindful of the sensation in your legs, arms, chest, body, and neck as you carry yourself forward.

4. Now, pay attention to your surroundings. Is it a pleasant autumn day/a quiet neighborhood/an isolated block of buildings?

5. When other thoughts enter your head, don't entertain them. Put them out.

6. Once done, gauge your feelings.

- At the end of the walk, I feel (energized/calmer/focused/serene):

_____

_____

_____

_____

_____

_____

_____

_____

_____

_____

Exercise 79: Your Personal Weather Report

Let's learn to evaluate your feelings. Just like a weather report that delves deep inside you and connects with your feelings, learning to identify your moods is a good way to tame them and practice emotional self-regulation.

1. Sit quietly and deep breathe. Become observant of what's around you and what's brewing inside you. Connect with your thoughts; what are you thinking about at this moment?

2. Inhale and exhale; become conscious of your breath and your chest rising and falling. Sit still.

3. Become mindful. How do you feel? Can you name your feelings just like the weather? Stormy, sunny, cloudy, what is it?

4. We cannot change the weather; we accept it by adapting to it.

5. Your moods are the same, you cannot change them, but you can change the way you react to them. You are not defined by your moods.

6. Accept them, but do not let them control you. When it rains, we use an umbrella; we do not purposely walk in the rain unless we want to. Same with your mood, you can feel angry, but you can choose to lash out or be silent until the anger passes.

Document your experience

_____

_____

_____

_____

_____

_____

_____

_____

_____

_____

Exercise 80: Stress Tolerance For the Two Extremes

Pair breathing with muscle relaxation to calm down.

1. Deep breathe; inhale and fill your belly.

2. As you do, tense the muscles in your entire body.

3. Hold it and feel the tension.

4. Breathe out; as you do say, "relax," and feel your body go limp as the tension goes with it

5. Where else in your body do you still feel tense?

6. Repeat the exercise and concentrate on those tensions.

7. Practice until you learn to quickly release tension this way.

Document your experience

_____

_____

_____

_____

_____

_____

_____

_____

Exercise 81: Practice Healthy Venting

Venting is healthy, but venting when you are angry or highly emotional and hurt is not recommended; you barely have control of your emotions at this time. Venting in anger strengthens the neural connections between anger and violence, which is something you must avoid. Be mindful about whom you vent to, where, and also venting on social media.

Repeated venting can make you unpopular even among sympathetic friends and family who are affected by your constant complaints and barrage of frustrations. Therefore, practice skillful venting as shown in these four steps.

1. Choose to vent in private—write, draw, doodle, scribble in your journal, and put down all your thoughts, anger, frustrations, etc. Once done, re-read it. Do you still feel the same? Or does the situation look less volatile? On paper, emotions have a way of changing their perspective and losing some of their depth.

2. Avoid co-rumination; this happens when you vent to someone and the emotion you are feeling intensifies. You get no relief from the vent. What you do then is let go of control and step back, asking the other person their opinion.

"How can I change the way I feel about this problem? What do you suggest?"

3. Choose who you vent to. If you vented before to someone and they offer no solution or different perspective of the problem, they are not good candidates to vent to. Choose people who actively engage with you to help you gain a solution and change of perspective to help calm your mood.

4. Online venting is tricky. It will make you feel good to vent and call somebody out on social media, but your negativity could have mixed reactions. The gesture could also be viewed as bullying or an act of uncontrolled rage.

How I chose to vent:

_____

_____

_____

_____

_____

_____

_____

_____

How I felt after:

_____

_____

_____

_____

_____

_____

_____

_____

Exercise 82: Music to Calm My Soul

Music is a great partner for emotional regulation and friends of people dealing with BPD. However, just like your friends, it's important to choose your music, as different genres have different effects on your mood.

- When feeling anxious, angry, or distressed—play soothing, relaxing, and calm music.

- When feeling sad, disappointed, and let down—play happy, feel-good music.

What I felt, What I Played, and How the Music Made Me Feel:

My Emotion	Type of Music I Played	How I Felt After

Building Relationships Without Letting Mood Swings Interfere

Anxiety can build up and affect the way we feel as well as how we interact with others. Allowing anxiety, anger, annoyance, sadness, etc. to build results in the emotion bubbling over and causing you to react in a negative and unpleasant manner. Let's look at stopping mood swings from interfering with your relationships.

Exercise 83: Grounding Techniques to Reduce Anxiety

The 5,4,3,2,1 Technique: To Prevent Anxiety Building

Begin with deep breathing. Inhale for five seconds, hold your breath for five and exhale for five seconds. Repeat five times. Now begin your grounding technique.

5.	Identify five things you can see in your surroundings. A pen, clock, tree, clouds, etc.
4.	Identify four things you can touch or feel. The chair you're sitting on, your phone, a book, etc.
3.	Identify three things you can hear. A bird chirping, car horn, vacuum, laughter, etc.
2.	Identify a smell. Walk around if you must and look for something to smell. A pillow, perfume, soap, flowers, food, etc.
1.	Identify a positive fact about yourself. You're funny, loyal, methodical, artistic, kind, etc.

Note: At the end of the exercise, I realized my anxiety had left/diminished/etc. I let go of anxiety and focused more on my senses.

_____

_____

_____

_____

Exercise 84: Justify Mood Swings

This exercise will help to justify and understand reactions as well as the reactions of others.

Use the chart below to try and understand if your mood alterations were due to ANTs or purposeful.

Situation/Person or Event That Caused My Mood Shift. Do I Blame Outside Influences?	Were My Emotional Responses Triggered? Or was it an automatic negative thought?	Could I have controlled my mood if I had tried?	What Could I Have Done Differently?

Conflict Management Skills

Dealing with BPD means there are times you are fighting internal battles. Conflicts that are debated on the outside with other people and those on the inside which sometimes fester and grow.

Conflict Management the Difference in Responses

Healthy Responses	Unhealthy Responses
Practice empathy when considering others' opinions.	Not recognizing what's important for the other person and therefore responding in the negative.
Calm, serene, understanding responses.	Vicious, forceful, angry, and hurtful responses.
Willing to forgive. To forget and get over the conflict.	Instills fear of abandonment by rejecting love, trying to shame or isolate.
Willing to compromise and avoid retaliation and punishments.	Unreasonable, unwilling to see the other's point of view.

Conflict management is centered on emotional awareness and quick stress relief. This exercise will help you gain those skills and learn the difference between healthy and unhealthy responses.

Exercise 85: Quick Stress Relief Skills:

Remain balanced through these quick stress relief skills.

Engaging the Senses, Sight, Sound, Smell, Taste, and Touch to Relieve Stress:

- Enjoy the flavor of a relaxing cup of herbal tea.

- Squeeze a stress ball.

- Write in your journal or piece of paper, anything at hand.

- Deep breathe.

As you practice these skills become:

- Mindful of your own feelings.

- Read the body language of the other person correctly.

- Pay attention and listen to what the other person is saying.

- Communicate your point very clearly.

My thoughts: Today, I practiced quick stress relief, and the results were:

_____

_____

_____

_____

_____

_____

_____

Exercise 86: Emotional Awareness Skills

Become emotionally attuned to yourself to better understand others.

1. Identify your emotions:

Check on your emotional state throughout the day. Were you late for work? Did you get complimented on your recent project? Did your partner disappoint you? Etc. Make a note of your emotional changes to understand your type of response to different situations.

My notes: My emotional changes today and what caused them.

2. Pay attention to others' emotions:

Try to notice how other people around you are feeling. Unconsciously we tune into people when we realize someone is happy, angry, or sad. Now make a conscious effort to notice the emotions of people you interact with throughout the day.

My notes: Today, I noticed several emotional levels: (name the person, emotion, and your understanding of what may have caused the emotion.)

3. Let others know how you feel:

Talk about the emotion you are experiencing; it makes it easier to handle and also lets the other person know when they trigger your emotions.

My notes: Today, I was emotional because:

But I was able to express myself and my emotional state by:

Exercise 87: Emotions That Fit Facts

Use these tables to add your interpretations of facts you associate with emotion. Two examples are given for each emotion. Add more facts you associate with the emotion.

Anger:
E.g.:   • Not being able to control events or people as you want to.   • Thinking you have been treated wrong/unfairly/biased.
Reasons I associate with anger:

Envy

E.g.:

- Thinking others have more than they deserve.
- Wanting people who have what you don't have to experience loss, bad luck, etc.

Reasons I associate with envy:

Fear

E.g.:

- Thinking about the past.
- Fear of embarrassing yourself.

Reasons I associate with fear:

Disgust

E.g.:

- Being forced to do something you don't like.

- Dealing with someone you feel is inferior to you in intelligence.

Reasons I associate with disgust:

My notes: What I observed about my emotional state, how easily I associate negative emotions with situations/events/people, etc. What can I change?

_____

_____

_____

_____

_____

_____

_____

- Other emotions you can analyze this way: fear, sadness, shame, guilt, etc.

Self-Validation of Primary Emotions

If you feel hurt by something someone did, said, or an event and you don't validate feeling hurt that emotion is going to transform and evolve into perhaps anger, a secondary emotion.

Accepting and validating your primary emotion can often prevent an avalanche of emotional outbursts from resulting.

Exercise 88: Acknowledge Your Emotion

How do I feel right now? Name your emotion and acknowledge the root cause.

_____

_____

_____

_____

_____

_____

_____

_____

_____

_____

_____

_____

Exercise 89: Self-Validation

Accept your emotions.

E.g.: If I feel sad, it's okay because the situation is emotional

Choose and use the following statements to validate your emotion by reading them out loud. Add more that you can think of.

It is okay to feel this way right now.
Right now, I accept the emotion I am dealing with, but I will get over it.
I have every right to feel this way.
I am going to accept and feel this emotion, but it will not dictate how I behave
This is not a nice emotion, but I will not let it infect and hurt me.

———————◆———————

Working Your Mood Buttons—Preplanned Coping Skills

Learn to understand, forecast, and stop your moods before they manifest and cause trouble by preplanning your coping strategies. Explore within yourself and come up with solutions to cope with your sudden emotional changes.

Exercise 90: Finding Solutions to Manage My Moods

My Emotion	How I Can Cope
Feeling worthless	
Sudden anger	
Stress	
Low-energy mood	
Depressed	
Lonely	

Use these exercises to get to know your emotions and in time tame them. Practice and awareness will, in time, yield results.

The Story of Blake

Blake loved his family but could not connect with his kids and partner; he was seen as moody, angry, and almost an outsider by them. This hurt Blake, who lived to take care of them. He would sacrifice his comforts for the sake of his kids. He would work late to earn more to give his family comfort. He helped his wife with household chores and basically put his needs on the back burner to aid the welfare of his family. Yet, he could not connect with them, and he did not feel loved.

During an argument with his family about not being appreciated, Blake blurted out that he was exhausted and tired of taking care of their needs all the time. To this, his partner gently pointed out that in neglecting his needs, Blake lacked proper rest, time to himself, and opportunities to de-stress. His anger, irritability, and inability to let go and have fun was a result of it, and it pushed away his family.

Blake realized that his mood swings were tied to his lack of self-care, which canceled out the good he performed for his family. He managed to cut back, dedicate time to himself, and become happier, which resulted in positive interactions with his family.

Mood swings that push others away are only one downside of lacking emotional regulation. Out-of-control mood swings encourage impulsive behavior, which can put you in danger. Let's look at controlling impulsive and disruptive behavior next.

Chapter FIVE

How to Stop Impulsive Behavior That Puts You in Danger

If you wanna rebel, rebel out of responsibility, not recklessness—rebel out of accountability, not impulse.

- Abhijit Naskar

A lack of impulse and restraints leads to disruptive behavior which sometimes is fatal; reckle sex, impulsive eating when obese, and addictive behavior, such as drug addiction a gambling.

Leonard suffered from marital issues when his partner was unfaithful and left him; he soug refuge in alcohol and drugs as pain-numbing alternatives. He indulged in one-night stands a reckless driving intoxicated. One night he had an accident and ended up paralyzed from the wa down. His gambling had depleted his finances; he was alone and broke. His behavior did not bri his partner back, but he did end up losing much more. If Leonard had reigned in his emotions and destructive behavior, he might have moved on and met someone else. Envisioning a better turn of events where he was successful even after heartbreak, Leonard went into rehab, learned to walk again, and gained control of his impulses because he realized he could not control other people hurting him—but he could control himself.

Let's Learn About Impulse Control

Self-control or impulse control is your ability to take charge of your feelings and behavior. Let's categorize your mood control impulses as "freeze" and "melt." Freeze is a successful action that freezes the mood instead of acting on it. Melt is the point where you give in and match self-destructive behavior to the mood.

Exercise 91: Freeze or Melt Impulse Controls

Example answers are given for the first one. Add your melt/freeze reactions to the rest of the questions to practice your responses.

1. Your friends are having a heart-to-heart conversation about a marital problem one is having. You want to jump in and add your take on how you handled a similar problem.

Melt Action	Freeze Action
You interrupt the conversation to describe how you dealt with an unfaithful partner. As you vent, you lose control and forget about the friend seeking advice. You later recall the conversation and cringe in embarrassment, realizing you spilled more personal details than intended and that you butted in on your friend seeking help and advice.	You hold your tongue and listen patiently and gather the facts, then when there is a pause in the conversation, you gently tell your friend that you experienced a similar situation and that if she ever needs advice, you would be happy to help.

2. You just lost your job, and until you find another, you are on a tight budget, and in between, you get invited to your best friend's birthday. You go out shopping with a maximum spending allowance. Suddenly, you see a pair of shoes you wanted (not needed) on sale at $250, and you suddenly develop an impulse to splurge. What do you do?

Melt Action	Freeze Action

3. You are doing well working on a project in the office due in three days, and suddenly the boss asks you if you can help train a rookie, which is a full-time project. You know you must complete your project, but you also want to take on the rookie because you were asked. What do you do?

Melt Action	Freeze Action

4. You are out for a drive, and you suddenly get the urge to test your car to see how far it can go, but it's raining. Your urge to try something dangerous is very high. Do you play it safe or give in?

Melt Action	Freeze Action

5. It's boys' night out, but you resolve to stop at one drink. As the night moves on, you feel relaxed and like experimenting with hallucinogens and maybe chatting someone up. Is it a good idea? What do you do?

Melt Action	Freeze Action

Learning to Create Awareness Between Impulses and Actions

Acknowledge your impulses, feel them, and know they exist but do nothing beyond. The skill helps you to acknowledge your thoughts, sensations, and emotions but not take action to stop them, hide them, or control them; thus, you are creating a barrier between feeling impulses and acting on them.

Exercise 92: Mindful Walking Down the Street Exercise

Begin by closing your eyes and deep breathing for five minutes.

Step 1. Now you are going to imagine you are walking down a street you know. As you continue your walk, you suddenly see someone you know, and you wave. But they don't wave back. They ignore you and walk right past you. Reflect on that moment for a while.

Step 2. Let's reflect on the scenario you imagined and think back to the incident of the person you knew not acknowledging you.

- What did you feel at that moment?

- What emotions overtook?

- What impulses came over you?

Now think about all those thoughts and emotions you were dealing with. How did it affect your behavior? Or at least, how would it have made you feel?

My thoughts and feelings on this exercise:

_____

_____

_____

_____

_____

_____

Was this exercise beneficial in reigning in your emotions and impulses connected to them?

_____

_____

_____

_____

_____

_____

_____

_____

_____

Visualizing Alternate Reactions to Your Impulsive Behavior

Visualizing alternate reactions to emotion and the following impulse helps you see how far our reactive behavior can affect a situation.

Exercise 93: Visualize Your Impulsive Behavior

Choose a time of day when your mind is calm and you feel relaxed.

- Sit down and practice deep breathing for three minutes.

- Visualize a scene where someone is disrespecting you.

  - Your kids are not paying attention to you when you ask them to calm down and finish their breakfast as you have to drop them at school and leave for work.

  - Your co-worker has taken sole credit for the project you helped them make a success.

  - Any other scenario that instigates an impulsive behavior, emotion, or perhaps anger.

- Remember, you are in a calm frame of mind, but right now, you visualize your behavior matching your impulses—to lash out in anger.

Write down your visualization:

What do you feel after imagining yourself reacting to the impulse?

- Was it necessary?

- Avoidable?

- Could you have handled it differently?

———◆———

Distress Tolerance Pros and Cons: To Not Make the Situation Worse

Pros and cons help you to think about the advantages of engaging in a certain behavior and not. Because let's face it, there are some reactions that are necessary and some that can lead to bigger problems.

Exercise 94: Pros and Cons of Distress Tolerance Skill

This exercise helps you to think about the advantages and the disadvantages of a behavior.

Tips:

- Choose a time you are not in a crisis to practice this skill.

- Try to identify the behavior that is the problem.

- Write down your pros and cons; have them as a guide to refer to.

_____

_____

_____

_____

Example chart:

	PROS	CONS
Enjoying a glass or two of whisky	• De-stress and relax • Avoid feeling negative • Short-term high • No health risks	• Losing focus temporarily • Possibility of forming an addiction • Health risks when indulged long term • Not a good example for kids
Not indulging: Not drinking alcohol at all	• Learn to use healthy coping mechanisms • Sense of accomplishment in avoiding alcohol • A good example to kids • Choosing a healthy option	• Not having a quick de-stress outlet • Being irritable and high strung • Dealing with extreme emotions

This chart shows you the advantages and disadvantages of having a glass of whisky. As you can see, it's not all bad within limits, which is typical of the distress tolerance skill I want you to learn.

Use the example chart to write out your go-to impulse activities and hash out the advantages and disadvantages of each one.

1. Impulse Activity	PROS	CONS
Not indulging:		

- Note: How can I manage this impulse activity without making it destructive?

_____

_____

_____

_____

_____

_____

_____

2. Impulse Activity	PROS	CONS
Not indulging:		

- Note: How can I manage this impulse activity without making it destructive?

3. Impulse Activity	PROS	CONS
Not indulging:		

- Note: How can I manage this impulse activity without making it destructive?

_____

_____

_____

_____

_____

_____

DBT Chain Analysis Skill

Learn about destructive behavior and the events that led to it by using this skill. It is a good tool for uncovering all the links or factors responsible for the final destructive behavior.

Exercise 95: Chain Analysis Worksheet

THE CHAIN

4. Vulnerability

⇅

2. Prompting Event

⇅

⇅

3. Links

⇅

⇅

1. Problem Behavior

⇅

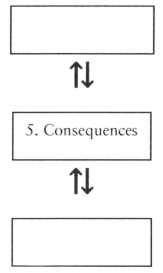

5. Consequences

1 Problem Behavior, Responsible for the Consequences That Followed	**5** Consequences
➡️ • Identify the problem event you wish to change.	 • What happened as a result of your problem behavior?

2 Prompting Events, What are the Links?

- What caused your problem behavior?

3 Links to the Problematic Behavior

- What are the events, including emotions, actions, thoughts, body language, etc., that occurred after the prompting event and then led to your problem behavior?

4 Vulnerability Root Cause is Connected to the Prompting Event

When the prompting event took place, what was it that made you vulnerable? It could be external, internal, or both.

My Observations on what types of events instigate my prompts:

_____

_____

_____

_____

_____

_____

_____

_____

_____

_____

_____

_____

———————◆———————

Replacing Your Impulsive Behavior

With this skill, you can identify and replace your destructive negative behavior with another that's more positive.

Exercise 96: Impulsive Habit Reversal Training Skill

This skill works by training yourself to recognize an impulse and then change it; let's say you suddenly get an impulse to get online and make a few purchases, although you are on a budget. What you do is replace it with something else. You decide to practice mindful walking. Get out of the house, away from the computer, and walk.

My Frequent Impulses	What I Can Replace Them With

My notes: Today, I tried impulse reversal:

_____

_____

_____

_____

_____

_____

_____

✦

Maintaining Balance in Wants and Shoulds

There are things we enjoy and want to do, and there are things we do because we should. It's important to maintain a balance of both. Too many wants and you neglect what's important, too many shoulds, and you become frustrated—equality is important.

Exercise 97: Balancing Wants and Shoulds

In this chart are key areas in your life that need taking care of, write down your wants and needs against each one. Try to maintain equality between the two for a healthy balance by deciding on the importance of the wants and shoulds.

*Example for the first is given.

Key Areas of My Life that Need Attention. Compare your wants and needs against each area.	WANTS	SHOULDS
My partner	E.g.: Intimacy, love, financial security	E.g.: Be understanding, give attention
Kids		
Spiritually		

Job Requirements		
Finances		
Leisure		
Exercise		

Household Chores/Duties		
Health Requirements		
(add more as needed)		

My notes: Since creating a balance between my wants and shoulds, I have found a change in my relationships:

_____

_____

_____

_____

_____

_____

_____

_____

_____

_____

_____

The Marshmallow Experiment—Delayed Gratification

A marshmallow is kept in front of kids who were asked to wait 15 minutes without giving in to temptation. Those who wait get double the quantity which is the benefit of delayed gratification.

In DBT, this technique works to reduce destructive behavior. For example, you can plan a movie and dinner with friends on the weekend rather than a weekday, which delays temptations associated with destructive behavior interfering with your set goals—eating healthy, saving money, and being more productive on weekdays.

Examples of delayed gratification:

- Buying the latest iPhone a year after it's released at a lower price.

- Going on holiday in summer by saving on entertainment and going out every weekend.

- Adding your bonus to your retirement fund and living comfortably at a later stage rather than making a downpayment on a new car (which you don't need).

Exercise 98: Delayed Gratification Skills

Use the chart below to see how delayed gratification can help you avoid destructive unproductive behavior. The first example is given. Add more areas you can reap the benefits of delayed gratification.

My Immediate Gratification That Can Lead to Destructive Behavior	My Delayed Gratification Reward
E.g.: This year, I plan to buy all new Christmas decor and dress up my house elaborately.	If I wait for the after-Christmas sales, I can buy plenty of decor for next year at half price and use the money I save this year to treat my family to a wonderful Christmas dinner.

Exercise 99: Press Pause Skill

Learn to dial down your responses to your impulses.

- Making sudden decisions without thinking them through.

- Jumping in and interrupting a conversation.

- Becoming too passionate and losing control during a debatable conversation.

Impulse Control Skills

Practice these skills the next time your impulses are triggered

1. Deep breath. Turn away from the trigger and deep breathe a few times until you feel your heartbeat slowing down.
2. Tell yourself to stop before you even react and visualize a pleasant outcome to the episode.
3. Acknowledge your emotions but do not react; start to count back from 10 to 1.
4. Be honest with yourself. Do you really want the situation to escalate, or do you want a peaceful settlement?

My Notes: Today, I practiced my impulse control skill and:

_____

_____

_____

_____

_____

_____

_____

_____

Exercise 100: Managing Destructive Urges

With so many people dealing with BPD, it is best to start with compromise from your end. is not surrendering but rather an amicable solution to an otherwise unpleasant situation b managing your impulsive and destructive behavioral urges before they cause damage and trigge reactions in the other person, leading to the whole snowball effect of problems.

Step 1: Visualize What Would Happen If You Were to Give Into Your Destructive Behavior. What Would the Consequences Be?
Your friend invites you to a buffet at the corner restaurant after work; you are trying to get your diabetes in control, but the buffet sounds tempting, especially since you have been controlling your food. But then you remember what the doctor said and imagine losing control and indulging at the buffet. You can see the medical tests showing a huge spike in your blood sugar, which motivates you to decline the offer and go home to a healthy and satisfying meal.
Step 2: Stand Aside and Observe
Now that you decided not to get tempted by the buffet meal offer, you are not really craving all those calorie-dense treats. You are merely considering but not really interested because you did not *give in* to the urge to want to treat your food cravings.
Step 3: Visualize the Positive
Go back to considering the invite to join your friend for the buffet, but this time, visualize refusing, sticking to your healthy meal plan, and visiting the doctor with your fresh report. He gives you an 'A-okay' and even reduces your meds which makes you feel happy and accomplished.

Can you see how just five minutes of visualization can stop your impulse to give in to destructive urges and reward you with positive outcomes to look forward to in the future?

Today, I practiced visualization to stop my impulsive urges. These are the results:

Step 1: Visualize What Would Happen If You Were to Give Into Your Destructive Behavior. What Would the Consequences Be?
Step 2: Stand Aside and Observe
Step 3: Visualize the Positive

Exercise 101: Mindfulness Meditation to Control Impulses

Gain control of your emotions, thoughts, and behavior through mindfulness meditation. Being in the present helps to regulate your thoughts and emotions; to become aware of what's going on and to look at situations more objectively.

- Name your thoughts and emotions. Let's say you feel a sudden surge of anxiety and defeat. Become mindful of the impulse to react.

- Name the emotion—"anger." Why do you want to retaliate?

Because

Anger means →	And accepting disrespect means →	Vulnerability/giving in because I did not fight back. OR Better control of my impulses and avoid a situation I would regret later.

What is the positive side of controlling my anger (impulse)? What did I gain?

_____

_____

_____

_____

_____

_____

Exercise 102: Journal Prompts

Use the following prompts as reflective questions in your journal entry when trying to resolve a situation that triggers your impulsive behavior. (E.g., a disrespectful boss who makes you angry and want to quit your job.)

1. How will I feel if I go ahead and do this right now?

   (E.g.: how will I feel if I resign right now?)

   _____

   _____

   _____

   _____

   _____

   _____

   _____

   _____

   _____

2. Will I feel happy, panicked, sad, etc., by tomorrow?

   (E.g.: will I regret my hasty decision tomorrow?)

   _____

   _____

   _____

   _____

_____

_____

_____

_____

_____

_____

_____

_____

_____

3. If I control myself and do not give in to my urge to react, how will I feel tomorrow? (E.g.: If I don't quit today, how will I feel?)

_____

_____

_____

_____

_____

_____

_____

_____

4. In the past, when I gave in to hasty decisions, were there consequences I didn't like?

    (E.g.: have my hasty decisions in the past had negative effects on me, how easy is it to find another job?)

Let's end with a lesson from Leonard, who gained control of his destructive behavior by visioning a positive outcome to his situation a little late, but he did get there. He even went to the extreme of tattooing the word 'no' on his arm—a bleak reminder to say 'no' to his impulses.

Leonard was lucky, he could turn around his reckless behavior, but sometimes we are not that fortunate. Self-harm has long and short-term effects, sometimes fatal, with terrible consequences taking place in an instant. But you can learn to protect yourself.

Chapter SIX

Protecting Yourself From Self-Harm or Suicide

All things are difficult before they are easy.

- Thomas Fuller

Not everyone dealing with BPD will attempt suicide. Some are contemplating, and others are threatening to do so. Yet it is a dangerous game with fire.

We mentioned that 1% to 2% of the general population suffer from BPD. Out of the figures:

- 70% attempt suicide

- 10% are successful (Harmer et al.)

Let's strive to reduce those bleak figures. The exercises listed here are designed to help you reframe your self-destructive thoughts and behavior and get to their root causes.

———◆———

Dealing With Severe Depression

Mindful practices that help deal with overwhelming thoughts can help get over severe depression.

Exercise 103: Mindfulness Breathing for Severe Depression

Slow your breathing and heart rate to overcome the sudden panic and anxiousness that overtakes you.

- Find a quiet spot with no distractions. Sit or stand with your head, heart and pelvis aligned; sit/stand up straight, chest out, and shoulders back. Close your eyes for better concentration.

Gently inhale to a count of four and draw the breath up slowly.
At the top of the inhale, pause and hold for one second.
Mindfully exhale very slowly for four seconds. Feel the breath leave your body.
Pause at the end of the exhale for one second. Repeat the steps.
Breathe until you feel a change in your mental and physical self.

- How I felt at the end of this exercise:

_____

_____

_____

_____

185

Exercise 104: Mindfulness of Colors

- The color blue emits short wavelengths and lowers blood pressure and heart rate (Stern e al.).

- Did you know that the LED lights used at Japanese train stations have reduced suicide rate by 74%? (Matsubayashi et al.).

Other colors wield psychological influences over us and can be used for their benefit.

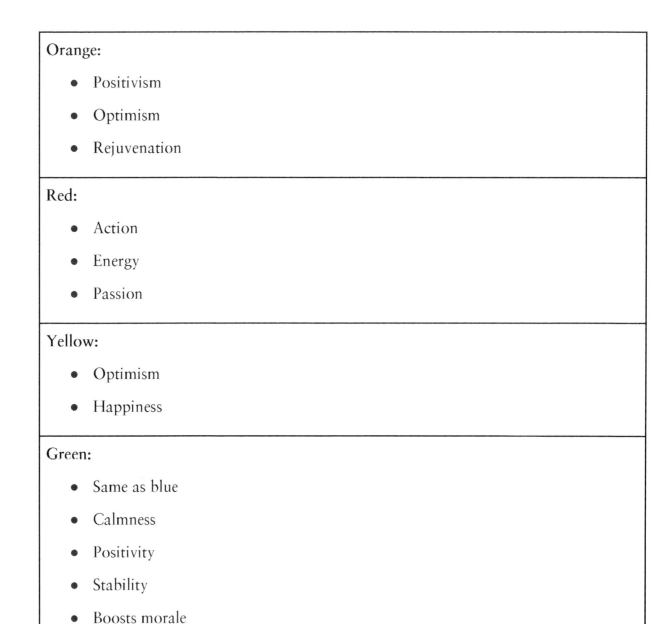

Orange:
- Positivism
- Optimism
- Rejuvenation

Red:
- Action
- Energy
- Passion

Yellow:
- Optimism
- Happiness

Green:
- Same as blue
- Calmness
- Positivity
- Stability
- Boosts morale

Exercise 105: Urge Surf Skill

Use this skill whenever faced with thoughts of self-harm.

- Sit with the urge, thinking about it for five minutes. Set a timer.
- At the end of the timer, has the urge reduced?
- No? Set the timer for another five minutes.
- Repeat until the self-harm urge has passed.

Exercise 106: Handling the Immediate Crisis

Deal with ongoing distress using this worksheet.

Coping Solution 1: Don't fight it; accept the distress.   Do not judge, react emotionally, or agree. Simply acknowledge the distress. Sit with it but do not engage. Accept that events happened to make you feel this way.
Coping Solution 2: Detract and create a new sensation.   Distract yourself from the destructive behavior urges by drastic maneuvers. Punch a pillow, run iced water over your hands, use a red pen to write on your body or create cut-like marks, anything to detract from the situation.
Coping Solution 3: Avoid feeling pain.   Engage in feel-good activities to drown out the pain.   • Listen to music.   • Paint.   • Watch a comedy sketch.   • Write a letter to someone you love.

Coping Solution 4: Self-soothe.

Indulge in some TLC.

- Take a hot bath.

- Read a book.

- Lie in bed while you play music.

- Enjoy a warm/cool drink.

- Play with your pet.

Radical Acceptance

This is the belief that accepting a painful event will make it less painful.

Exercise 107: Ten Steps of Radical Acceptance

1. Stop Fighting Reality Saying or thinking, "this should not be happening to me," is denying reality, which is more painful to accept.
2. Be Realistic Accept it. Tell yourself, "This is reality, I can't change it!"
3. Dissect the Event Try to figure out the chain of events that led to the incident for better understanding.
4. Accept Wholeheartedly accept with your mind, body, and soul. No remaining doubts. Radical acceptance is acknowledging it all.

5. **What Would You Do If You Accepted the Truth?**

Write it all down.

6. **Visualize Dealing With Reality**

Visualize your acceptance of reality and the pain that's inevitable.

7. **Feel Your Bodily Reactions**

How does your body feel as you accept the reality of the situation? Tension leaves? Slumped? Etc.

8. **Channel the Pain**

Like a river, allow the painful emotions to flow through you; cry if it helps, and let the anger, sadness, despair, and so on wash over you.

9. **Understand the Value of Life**

Even though you are in pain, there are still reasons to go on living.

10. **Make a List of Good and Bad**

If you find yourself disagreeing with the above points, make a list of good and bad points.

xercise 108: Improve Using Positive Imagery

e your imagination to turn a bad situation positive.

Imagine	Visualize a positive outcome of the distressing event.
Meaning	Take the painful situation and find meaning for it.
Relax	Practice relaxation techniques.

Pray	Follow up on your beliefs in a higher power.
Focus on one	Become mindful of one thing and focus on that.
Encourage	Talk to yourself and clarify the situation.
Take a break	Leave the situation; step outside, stop thinking about it, and engage in other activities.

Exercise 109: Establishing Safe People Skill

Use the box to add the names of people you feel safe to talk to, be with, call in an emergency, et

You can write their names or draw them.

---

xercise 110: Journal Prompts—Practice Talking to People

hese journal prompts will help you to practice talking and dealing with other people and their wn emotional dysfunction when you are thinking of self-harm.

- "Why did they react aggressively toward me? Did I do or say something?"

- How did I feel at that moment?

_____
_____
_____
_____
_____
_____
_____
_____

- Did they have a point? Was there a reason for their reaction and response?

_____
_____
_____
_____
_____
_____
_____
_____

- Could they have reacted differently or said something else to help me?"

- Was what they said helpful to me? Could they have offered better advice or reacted differently?"

_____

_____

_____

_____

- I wonder if they know that they hurt me or if their answer did not solve my problem?"

_____

_____

_____

_____

_____

_____

_____

_____

- If I could see them again, what would I say to them now?"

_____

_____

_____

_____

_____

Exercise 111: Letting Go of Judgements

Negative judgments of ourselves by us remain to fester and grow. Judgments you *assume* other people bestow on you are harshly critical and toxic.

Use this chart to identify self-judgments and stop the attacks.

Think of a Judgment You Are Dealing With, and Describe it in Detail	How Does the Judgment Make You Feel? What Emotions Are You Dealing With?	What if You Did Not Include This Negative Judgment in Your Life? How Would it Be?

Exercise 112: The Box of Self-Harm

Increase your emotional awareness using this exercise to identify with words that describe your emotional self.

My Box of Self-Harm Is...

(Circle the appropriate words and add any you feel need to be there)

Betrayed	Low	Angry
Bitter		
	Guilty	Confusing
Fearful	Purified Worrying	

Bitter		Hurt		
				Embarrassed
	Painful	Awkward		
Young				
Shameful				
	Low	Exhausted		Weary
Lonely				
High		Survival	Highlighted	

The Wise Mind

DBT identifies the mind in three stages;

- The reasonable mind for solving a problem intellectually.

- The emotional mind functions on feelings, thoughts, and behavior.

- The wise mind, a balance of both reason and emotion in combination, is the middle path that encourages using left and right brain activity.

Exercise 113: Recalling an Experience Using the Wise Mind

Step 1: Settle into a quiet corner. Take five deep breaths. Recall a problem you are facing. No jc satisfaction, boredom, you are lonely, etc.

- Think about the problem, its roots, links, and consequences.

- Set a time frame (5 minutes).

- Think about a solution for the problem, let the answer come to you, and do not judge criticize.

- Accept the gut feeling you get, a sense of "this is the answer."

- Become aware of the answer your wise mind gave you.

Document your experience.

_____

_____

_____

_____

_____

_____

_____

Reach For a Life-Line

Every life matters and suicidal thoughts do not define your worth. Reach out to a professional when the urge to self-harm is too great because there is so much more positivity to gain in life than loss; you just need help finding it.

- Dial 988 Suicide and Crisis Lifeline and choose life.

What's next...

Emptiness can often take over and rob you of enthusiasm, which leads to boredom and procrastination. Let's look at overcoming this problem.

Document your experience.

Chapter SEVEN

What to Do When Nothing Fills the Emptiness

The two enemies of human happiness are pain and boredom.

- Arthur Schopenhauer

Feelings of emptiness, not understanding a sudden lack of energy, and simply not wanting bother too much with anything are symptoms brought on by boredom.

Jenna, for example, worked from home. A freelance cosmetics distributor, Jenna earne good commission on her sales but lacked interaction with others as her office was her home. S would often make plans to join an aerobics class, have dinner at that famous Italian spot, or off on a weekend adventure. Sadly, Jenna always found an excuse to cancel, stay home, or akeout, and watch a movie. She was constantly bored and unmotivated to take up any activity. And so, her life moved on quite uneventfully until depression became a partner.

Can you identify with Jenna?

Use these exercises to keep your mind active, alert, and enthusiastic about savoring new xperiences.

Finding Fulfillment With Mindfulness

Fill your life with outside experiences and let other people in to truly start living.

Exercise 114: Activities to Create a Sense of Fulfillment

Choose an activity or experience from the list and follow through.

- Adopt a pet.
- Volunteer for charity work.
- Find a partner to love or a friend to share your life with.
- Talk to a safe person about your feelings of emptiness, and try to find a reason why.
- Join a community: a local hobby club, a church of your faith, an adventure club, etc.
- Have you experienced a loss recently if you find ways to overcome your sadness; talk to friends and family, or immerse yourself in helping others.
- Face reality if you are dealing with substance abuse.
- Get a diagnosis to verify you may be dealing with BPD.

e action I took was...

elped me to:

_____

_____

_____

_____

_____

_____

_____

_____

_____

_____

_____

_____

Mindful Eating

This is a good practice to learn to appreciate minor details in life and focus your senses.

Practice the raisin technique discussed in exercise 30 to learn about mindful eating. You c substitute any food you like.

Exercise 115: The Leaf Experiment

This is a simple mindfulness exercise involving a leaf.

- Take a leaf, any type.

- Now analyze it; the color, texture, and pattern.

- Use your senses; sight, touch, and smell.

- Focus on the leaf for five minutes.

- Try to let go of outside thoughts and bring your focus down to only the leaf.

Today, I did the leaf experiment, and it made me feel appreciated because if a simple object like a eaf can have awesome characteristics, how complex and amazing are mine?

ACCEPTS Skills for Creating Wise Mind Distractions

Distracting tools are helpful for short-term avoidance of problems, giving you a chance to step away from a problem, refresh your mind and tackle it freshly. However, long-term avoidance of problems is not recommended as it may lead to bigger problems.

ACCEPTS is a good acronym for remembering the various coping mechanisms available.

A=Activities	Enjoy yourself: Meet friends, go for a walk, go to the beach, watch your favorite movie, listen to a music track, or call a friend for a long chat.
C=Contributing	Give back: Volunteer charity work, comfort a friend in need, donate clothes, books, etc., be kind to someone, help a friend.
C=Comparisons	Learn to appreciate: You may feel down now, but you didn't always feel this way, and it will pass. Think about all the people with similar or bigger problems than you.
E=Emotions	Feel: Trigger your emotions to feel alive, not numb and bored. Watch a sad movie, read a scary novel, listen to powerful music, and so on.
P=Pushing away	No matter what your problem is, try pushing it aside for a while to enjoy a breather.
T=Thoughts	Indulge your thoughts: Repeat the lyrics of a song, count back from 100, read a thought-provoking essay, or watch a film with a deep meaning.
S=Sensations	Stimulate your senses: Enjoy a warm bath, listen to smooth music, and squeeze a stress ball.

My experience using ACCEPTS skill:

_____

_____

_____

Exercise 116: Online Courses to Combat Boredom

Online courses are great for filling in gaps where you have nothing to do while learning a new skill. They are flexible and most often short-term, can be picked up when you want to and paused when you need time off.

Courses cover a variety of subjects, from accounting and business management to arts, and sciences and just about any type of subject you want to specialize in.

These courses are highly affordable and offer flexible payment options.

What Makes Our Interactions Feel Empty?

Block listening habits do just that; then block what the other person is saying because we are not really paying attention to what they are saying but responding in what we think is a appropriate manner.

- Which block listening habits are you most guilty of? Mark them with an X.

Block Listening Habits	Add X if 'yes'	Why is this habit bad?
Placating: Agree too many times, offering too many approving comments.		
Identifying: Quickly referencing what the other person is saying about a similar experience you had.		
Comparing: You are talking to the other person but subconsciously trying to determine which one of you is smarter.		
Derailing: Changing the subject to a more suitable one that stops the other person and allows you to talk.		
Being right: This fact could be stopping you from actively listening to what the other person is saying because you are right and *cannot* be wrong.		
Sparring: Pushing your opinion as correct and arguing when the other person disagrees.		

Advising: When not wanted, offering advice to a person who simply wants to vent about their problems.		
Daydreaming: You drift away because something the other person said triggered a memory of something else, and you revisit that incident.		
Judging: Having a negative opinion already formed about the other person and listening to them critically.		
Filtering: Only acknowledging certain parts of the conversation, taking note of only information you are interested in.		
Rehearsing: Preparing to talk and thinking about what to talk about even before the other person has stopped talking.		
Mind reading: You are zoning out because as soon the other person starts talking, you have already predicted what they are going to say.		

y most frequent block listening habits are:

_____

_____

_____

_____

_____

They tell me that I am:

_____

_____

_____

_____

_____

_____

_____

And I can fix it by:

_____

_____

_____

_____

———————◆———————

Identifying Unhealthy Relationships

Unhealthy relationships that feel "empty" could be an indication of your emotio
dependence. It could mean you depend on the other person to feel 'good,' and that is neve
healthy option.

You must learn to accept who you are, improve your behavior and cultivate a sense of in
peace and individuality that is not dependent on how anyone else makes you feel.

Exercise 117: Developing Emotional Independence

This exercise will teach you to become emotionally independent and stop relying on others to define your moods.

Use the statements for self-reflection and thinking of how differently you can handle the situations.

How Can I Learn to Accept Myself for Who I am?

- What are the benefits of being my biggest fan?

Learn to be more accepting of yourself by being less judgmental, avoiding criticizing your every move, and feeling guilty for things beyond your control. Become aware of who you are, look for plus points, and expand on your good skills. Strive for inner serenity and peace, slow down when needed and practice your mood-regulating skills.

Yes, I can learn to accept myself by:

_____

_____

_____

_____

_____

_____

_____

_____

_____

- Think, why do you judge yourself so harshly?

Is there a reason why you find it difficult to accept yourself? Is it a valid reason? Listen to the voices in your head that are constantly telling you, you are not good enough. Whose voices are they? Your parents, friends, etc.? How true do YOU think what they say is? Write down your thoughts and reasons for accepting these judgments of others.

Maybe it's time to start listening to myself and accepting all my good points:

_____

_____

_____

_____

_____

_____

_____

_____

- **Re-think Your Past**

If you figured your harsh self-judgments have a root cause in what your parents said or did, you might want to rethink their judgments and criticism. After all, they were on a learning curve too, they did not take a course in being great parents, so perhaps their judgments are not all correct and have no basis. Maybe your loss of self-worth comes from rejection, but is that person so worthy of you wallowing in anger, self-pity, and sadness? Maybe not? Maybe they deserve to be pitied. What are your thoughts on tying your emotional dependence on these other people? Can they really control your mind, or are you independent enough to change the way you think?

I need to let go of the past by:

_____

_____

_____

_____

- Stop Holding Grudges

If you learn to forgive and forget, you will be less burdened with the opinions and thoughts of others. You are then free to accept yourself for who you are. You not only become emotionally independent, but you also cultivate resilience to outside influences.

Try to understand that while you cannot control how another person acts, you can control the way you think about their behavior toward you. It becomes easier to forgive when you stop taking on the other person's behavior in a personal context. Their behavior is their responsibility to bear and not yours. But you can forgive and forget. Also, keep in mind that while forgiving and forgetting, you must develop a better understanding of how people behave and react, modifying your expectations of them as well as how much you are willing to invest in them.

I can learn to forgive and forget by:

- Enjoy Your Own Company

This means being alone with your thoughts, not using your smartphone or another stimulus to keep your mind occupied. Spend time with your thoughts and allow all those random ideas, suggestions, questions, etc., to pop into your mind. Dedicate this time to run through them, sort through them and file them away as solved. You will be surprised at how interesting the thoughts that run through your mind can be. Give in and savor them. Try to allocate at least 20–30 minutes a day for self-reflection.

My random thoughts tell me that:

- Get to Know Yourself

Just because someone says you have a great voice does not make you a good singer. You must know you have a voice worthy of training and projecting to help you sing like a nightingale.

That is just one example; what do you really know about yourself?

- What are your skills?

- What interests you?

- What things fascinate you?

- What do you dislike?

- What are your strongest beliefs?

- What are the values you strive to live by?

Today, I discovered so much about myself, I believe I am special because:

Learning to Say "No" When You Don't Need Help

Do you often end up exhausted because you have gone above and beyond your call of duty? Do you end up taking on one more project, an extra chore, or added responsibility because you simply cannot say, "Sorry, but *no,* I am unable to do so."?

Well, you are not alone. There are several people who struggle with the dilemma of refusing to take on more than what they are comfortable with and end up burnt out, dissatisfied, and failing to be there for the people that really matter.

The following exercise will teach you to say "no" in order to create more time for projects, events, and people you want to say "yes" to without getting emotionally involved.

Exercise 118: Deciding When to Say "No"

Have compounded reasons for saying "yes," or "no":	How do I relate to this situation?
Knowing what you want to do is important to be able to say a firm "no." But if you are in two minds about the request, you may end up saying "yes," although the healthy option for you would have been a "no." E.g.: Your colleagues ask you to join their project and help with the brainstorming session. You are already working on two other projects that take up most of your time. You only have weekends left, and using that means sacrificing your family time, but you feel the project may highlight you as hard-working, although everyone already knows you are hardworking. You accept anyway and immediately regret your decision.	
Appreciate and thank: Feel appreciated and proud someone asked you for help but not obliged enough to say "yes" when you don't want to. A "thank you, but I'm sorry" will serve you better if it is not the right time for you to take on more responsibilities.	I can learn to appreciate being needed but not give in to every request.

Avoid Offending the Other Person Let the other person know you are rejecting the project/task, etc., and not them as a person. Show them your appreciation and follow up with a good explanation of why you must say "no."	I can practice saying "no" without offending the other person.
Be Firm and Don't Give In We all know the people who won't take "no" for an answer and will try to wear you down into saying "yes," but maintain your self-respect and resolve to say a justified "no" by carefully explaining why you simply cannot. Be firm but appreciative of their request without giving in.	I can learn to tackle pushy people even though I could not before. I will also resolve to put forth my reasons and stick to my initial answer.
Accept the Losses Fear of missing out often makes us say "yes." E.g.: The fear of losing the revenue from a new project, although you are fully booked, the fear of not feeling included although you are too tired to attend the concert.	I can learn to accept the losses that come with me saying "no" when it is not practical for me to say "yes."

This type of fear of missing out makes us say "yes." Let go of that fear and accept that there will be losses. You cannot manage it all, but you can enjoy what you are dealing with at the moment by giving it your 100%.	
Practice If the word "no" is not part of your vocabulary, practice saying it. Do so in front of a mirror. Shout out, "no." Or find situations where you can say "no." E.g.: When the service person asks if you want more cheese on your pizza. Your kids ask if you can take them to the park when you are dealing with a bad headache, your friend asks you to join them for yoga when you want to go watch a movie, etc. There will be times you need lots of courage to say "no." You may feel as though you are letting down people or not meeting their expectations of you. You may even have to endure some backtalk, But remember that you are only healthy, happy, and helpful when your mind and body are balanced, relaxed, and rested. So, cultivate the courage to stand firm for what you believe are your capabilities and limits.	Today, I practiced saying "no." And the results were:

Journaling to Add Meaning to Your Days

Living a life of purpose is hugely different from making your way minus a proper plan. Journaling prompts are a successful method for focusing on and learning more about the meaning and purpose of your life which will help you to live a happy and wholesome life.

Engaging in activities that make you happy, avoiding judgment, and having a critical view of yourself all empower you to face life and its challenges with purpose.

Exercise 119: Journaling Prompts for Regulating Emotions When Boredom Takes Over

1. Am I living a life that is true to who I am? If not, what can I change?

_____

_____

_____

_____

_____

_____

2. What do I consider a "happy life?" What must I do to achieve this?

_____

_____

_____

_____

_____

_____

3. What is my one greatest goal?

_____

_____

_____

_____

_____

_____

4. What recent events/factors do I have to be grateful for?

_____

_____

_____

_____

_____

5. My talents and strengths are…? And I can use them for:

_____

_____

_____

_____

_____

6. If I lived a life free from responsibilities or meeting financial needs, what kind of person would I be, and how would I live?

_____

_____

_____

_____

_____

_____

7. The things stopping me from achieving my dreams and goals are:

_____

_____

_____

_____

_____

8. What I appreciate the most in my life is:

_____

_____

_____

_____

_____

9. I believe I can change some factors to live a more meaningful life, they are:

_____

_____

_____

_____

_____

10. If I were to write a memorial to myself, it would read thus:

_____

_____

_____

_____

_____

_____

✦

etting Go of a Fixed Mindset

ixed mindset or a closed mindset limits your capabilities by thinking negatively.

"I cannot achieve that much…"

"This is the best I can do…"

To change this type of thinking, you must develop a growth mindset where you believe your nts, beliefs, and characteristics can be improved.

Each person possesses a different set of talents, interests, and even temperament. Therefore characteristics they cultivate must be based on these abilities.

Adopting such a growth mindset will help you to improve your life and achieve your dream and goals: the promotion you want, a healthy relationship, etc.

Let's look at some examples:

Fixed Mindset	Growth Mindset
"I will never master this concept, it's my weakness."	"If I change the way I approach the problem, I may achieve success."
"It's no use studying, I will never understand it all."	"I think they did not understand me the first time; I need to be clearer."
"Even if I try to be more active, they will not give me the promotion."	"I will study harder to achieve above-average grades."

Exercise 120: Changing My Fixed Mindset to a Growth Mindset

1. Become Mindful of Your Fixed Mindset and Put a Stop To It.

Watch out for the cues in the "voice" that says:

- If only you had the talent…

- You can always back out…

- It's not my fault…

Add examples of your fixed mindset "voice":

_____

_____

_____

_____

_____

2. Accept You Have a Choice

Become conscious of your ability to choose how you decipher criticism, opposition, and setbacks. And that your choice of interpretation can be positive (growth mindset) or negative (closed mindset).

Choose to listen to your fixed mindset voice which tells you that you need to rethink, revamp and reevaluate your situation.

Add your examples of what challenges/criticism/oppositions you can address through a growth mindset voice.

_____

_____

_____

_____

_____

_____

3. Talk to Your Problems in a Growth Mindset Voice

Debate your challenges using a growth mindset voice to deduce the pros and cons of a situation by talking to yourself.

Think positive:

"Maybe if I changed my perspective of the whole incident, I would understand their point better."

"By accepting responsibility for the mistake, I can ask for another chance to fix it."

Write below how you would talk to the fixed mind problems you listed in point one, in a growth mind voice.

_____

_____

_____

_____

4. Accentuate Your Growth Mindset Solutions

You can change your thinking by training your mind to listen to one particular strain of voic above the other. Automatically amplify the growth mindset voice and drown out the fixed mindse voice.

Make a resolve to:

- become accepting of your oppositions

- to learn from your mistakes, accept them, and try again

- acknowledge the criticism but not judge harshly and be open to accepting and findir solutions.

How do you plan to enhance your growth mindset?

_____

_____

_____

_____

_____

Exercise 121: Emotional Fulfillment Rules

Our overall well-being is centered on our emotional and physical well-being. To be truly hap and content with yourself, you need emotional fulfillment. Follow these ten steps to achieve tha

1. Do not compromise your values.

You have a set of values that keep you grounded. What you believe is fair, honorable, and corre Staying true to those thoughts gives you a sense of worth and individuality of who you are. not change them to accommodate a person or a situation.

Document your values.

_____

_____

2. Manifest your dreams

here is no harm in envisioning your dreams coming true. A huge part of success depends on your magination, where you envision your dreams coming true. Believe in the power of manifestation.

ocument your experience.

3. Surround yourself with positive people

People who bring out the best in you and make you feel loved, needed, and worthwhile are you need to boost your self-esteem and give you the courage to chase your goals while sticking your values. They are a positive influence that keeps your mind centered and happy.

cument your experience.

---

4. Look for everything positive in your life

Overshadow your negative thoughts, self-doubts, and fears by thinking about everythi-
positive in your life. Forget about what's not working by taking stock of everything else that
working out.

Make a list of all the good factors in your life right now.

---

5. Take time to do what you love

Increase your happiness by taking time to enjoy the things you like. It may be a vacation
the sea once a year, a ski trip, or even white water rafting; if it makes you happy, take time
indulge yourself.

---

6. Follow your calling

Or your heart. Do what you believe is right for you. Not what someone else believes is the best activity, job, or hobby for you. Don't be afraid to take a chance on what you believe is your true desire.

7. Believe you can make a difference

Get involved in activities that instill a sense of purpose in you. Whether it's helping the planet to heal, getting involved in charity work, and so on, choose to engage in work that makes you feel accomplished as a human being.

Document your experience.

_____

_____

_____

_____

_____

_____

8. Be prepared to accept change

Constantly improving and innovating yourself is the best method to stay ahead, fix your shortcomings, and encourage your growth mind. Don't avoid change; embrace it as an essential stepping stone toward your progress.

Document your experience.

_____

_____

_____

_____

_____

_____

_____

_____

_____

_____

_____

9. Change yourself and not others

You cannot control other people, but you can control your thoughts, emotions, and behavic
Therefore, take charge of your life and push yourself toward positive change, and external factc
will fall into place.

Document your experience.

_____

_____

_____

_____

_____

_____

10. Treasure the simple pleasures of life

Time with family, laughs shared with your friends, days you spend daydreaming, a
activities that leave you feeling overwhelmed with love and care are irreplaceable. Treasure
memories and store them away carefully to be used when you need an emotional boost.

My thoughts on emotional fulfillment rules and how they can help me:

Before closing this chapter, I must reiterate the exercises listed are not meant to be followed all at once. Choose the ones you feel will be the most helpful, and gradually work through them at your leisure.

Next, let's look at the most volatile emotion someone with BPD must deal with—anger issues. Although a common emotion we experience from time to time, anger for someone with BPD is a toxic weapon that goes beyond angry words and can hurt the people they care about the most.

Chapter EIGHT

Manage Anger That is Boiling Inside You

When angry, count to ten before you speak. If very angry, count to one hundred.

- Thomas Jefferson

---

oes your anger go beyond sudden mood swings to boil and bubble over as a toxic substance that harms anyone it's directed at?

A common emotion for all of us, anger can be hard to manage when you are dealing with D and the emotional dysfunctions that follow the condition. The emotion triggers aggressive avior patterns that can go beyond a few nasty words directed at other people. When out of trol, this hostile and violent behavior can cause a lot of pain, especially to the people you love.

Anger is an emotion that is instigated by someone else and soon turns negative when you t and give into your volatile emotions by screaming back at the other person that wronged you. That action is an immediate and automatic negative reaction that you can learn to overcome through simple mindful communication to help resolve the situation, therefore transforming it into a positive reaction.

Mindfully Dealing With Anger

Replacing your negative reactions to anger is the most successful path to managing your violent outbursts. Anger is common, and trying to avoid feeling the emotions altogether is not a task anyone can achieve; however, you can control your projection of the emotion. That is what guided anger control can do.

Begin by identifying the triggers. Once you do so, you are in better control of the emotion and its effects on you.

Exercise 122: Identifying My Anger Triggers

1. Write Down Triggers That Often Cause Your Anger
E.g.: Having to repeatedly keep reminding your partner to do the same chore, being sidelined at the office, people who disrespect your opinion, etc.
2. Damage Your Anger Has Caused Over the Years
E.g.: Broken friendships, having to change jobs constantly, becoming distrustful of people.

3. How Do You Normally Behave When You Are Angry? E.g.: You shut down the other person, you accuse and name-call, you become violent and throw stuff, you leave the house, etc.

My thoughts on point 1:

_____

_____

_____

_____

_____

My thoughts on point 2:

_____

_____

_____

_____

thoughts on point 3:

_____

_____

Exercise 123: Using the Feelings Thermometer for Anger Control

The anger thermometer helps to gauge the level of your emotional state, which can go from 'happy' to 'furious' when triggered. You identified your common anger triggers in exercise 12. It's also important to identify how the emotion evolved and the feelings that led to it.

If you acknowledge that you are furious at someone, you become mindful of the emotion and it helps to reign in your automatic reaction to being furious, which could be screaming back at the other person. But by telling yourself, "I'm furious with X right now, but I need to calm down," you are taking charge of your volatile emotion to channel your anger more positively.

Likewise, the feelings thermometer will help you to identify the steps which lead to the first feeling of rage. Anger is instigated by the action of others. Often, it builds up, going from feeling happy one moment to feeling frustrated, angry, and downright furious.

By becoming aware of the changes that are taking place within your emotional self, you may be able to put a stop somewhere in the middle before your volatile emotion evolves into a destructive outcome.

Feelings Thermometer	Common Causes That Lead to the Feeling Recall times and situations you felt each of the emotions
Happy	E.g.: spending time with my partner (emotional gratification)
Worried	E.g.: when they cancel a date because of work (disappointment)
Frustrated	E.g.: being alone (boredom)
Angry	E.g.: that my partner canceled the date (being let down)
Furious	E.g.: they should have tried to keep the date (emotional dependency, being unreasonable)

What are your common triggers for each feeling?

_____

_____

_____

_____

- Can you identify a pattern of how your feelings can go from happy to furious?

- At which point do you generally start feeling frustrated? What are the common events yc have listed that lead to frustration?

- Is there a point where you can become aware of your anger being triggered by frustration?

- Can you consciously decide to avoid a negative reaction once you do?

  E.g.: engage in deep breathing, counting exercises, and other distress tolerance skills discussed.

Exercise 124: Mindfulness Techniques for Anger

Use these three mindfulness techniques to help yourself calm down and turn a negative reaction into a positive outcome by dealing with your anger empathetically.

Reflect on the three factors as you practice mindfulness to try and overcome your anger.

RECOGNIZE	• Anger is not an emotion to be suppressed. Unacknowledged anger can increase my anxiety and lead to negative outbursts. • I may not be comfortable acknowledging this volatile behavior, but accepting that I am dealing with the emotion within myself will lessen its effects and give me more control over my anger.
REALIZE	• Realizing your self-worth. • I accept myself for who I am and acknowledge my right to be loved and respected. • Once you do so, your inner anger will lessen, which means it will not remain at surface level to boil over when triggered. • Feeling inadequate and disrespected are often the main causes of anger developing, but by practicing mindfulness, you can stay in the present, appreciating, forgiving, and forgetting.

Breathe	• Your breathing often represents your inner emotion, and anger is one emotion that is represented through your breathing; short and shallow breaths are often a sign of agitation, which indicates a disconnect between the body and the mind.
	• Breathing is also one of the best techniques for controlling your anger and using mindfulness to control anger. Return to the technique every time you need to mindfully convert your volatile and negative behavior into a passive one.
	• Remember that anger often blinds us to our actions, and becoming mindful will help us become aware, helping us stay in control.

Exercise 125: Practicing Mindfulness to Understand My Anger

Use this worksheet to study your anger, how you used mindfulness to control it and how much mindfulness helped.

Day of the Week	Incident That Made Me Angry	How I Used Mindfulness	How I Felt After
Monday			
Tuesday			
Wednesday			
Thursday			
Friday			
Saturday			
Sunday			
My notes:			

_____

Exercise 126: RESISTT Technique to Control Distress Caused by Anger

A volatile emotion like anger can cause distress and make you feel overwhelmed and confused, leading to negative urges that will make you engage in destructive behavior as well self-harm. The RESISTT technique offers seven methods to help you reign in those urges and n give in.

1. R=Reframe	Today I Used the Reframe Technique:	It Has Taught Me That I Can:
There are some situations you will be exposed to that make it hard to think in balanced terms, and everything is viewed in shades of gray and black.		
• Being backward when it comes to speaking to people.		
• Deciding your life is only going to get worse, etc.		
To Reframe means to give those black thoughts a refresh. A lighter outline where the situation can be looked at from a different perspective.		

Find the positive in that pool of negatives E.g.: I am not backward when it comes to speaking to people I have a lot in common with. So maybe I am selective and not shy/backward.		
2. E=Engage in a Distracting Activity Take your mind away from the thought that is causing you distress.	Today, I Used the Distracting Technique:	By Using the Distracting Technique, I Can:

Stop thinking about the person/situation that is upsetting you and get involved in distracting activities that bring you pleasure. • Go for a walk. • Listen to music. • Read a book. • Walk away from the volatile situation and call a friend. • Practice mindful meditation. • Cook a favorite dish. Anything that distracts you from the stressful situation.		
3. S=Someone Else Focus on someone else or something else that makes you feel a more pleasurable emotion: love, happiness, etc.	Today, I Shifted My Focus to Avoid Feeling Angry:	Shifting My Focus to Someone More Positive When I Feel Distressed Helps Me To:

Doing so can overshadow the distress and anger. Find a way to avoid the situation that's triggering your anxiety and anger and step away from it into a more friendly situation.		
4. I = Intense Sensations When the distress is too much to bear, use a counter move, an intense sensation that overpowers the emotion you are feeling.	Today I Used An Intense Sensation to Distract My Negative Emotion:	This Method Helps Me To:

• Cold shower • Running an ice cube around your face • Go out into the cold weather • Feel the heat of the sun on your face		
5. S=Shut Out Situations you cannot control are not worthy of your stress. Arguing endlessly with someone getting more agitated, finding out the	Today I Decided to Shut Out a Situation That Had No Positive Outcome.	The Shutting Out Technique Helps Me To:

meeting you worked overnight for is canceled, etc. Avoid feeling distressed by shutting out the unpleasant you can't control or find an immediate solution for. Take a raincheck and keep your emotions in a positive mode.		
6. T= Thoughts That are Neutral Mindfulness exercises work well for this technique, where you focus on a neutral thought that is in no way linked to any emotional factor.	I Practiced Neutral Thoughts Today:	Turning to Neutral Thoughts Helps Me To:

• Counting backward • Being mindful of your surroundings • Picking out particular colors from your environment • Counting your fingers Anything that is destructive and totally inconsequential.		
7. T=Take a Break A healthy break from stressful situations or one that has grown too mundane will help you to recalibrate and come back fresh. Just make sure the breaks are well spaced out and do not become a go-to tool whenever you feel overwhelmed.	I Decided to Take a Break Because:	I Find That Taking a Break is Helpful For:

Exercise 127: Progressive Muscle Relaxation Techniques

Do you notice how your muscles tense and tighten whenever you feel anxious, angry, or stressed? That feeling often remains, adding to the trauma you are enduring.

By practicing progressive muscle relaxation techniques often, you will be able to adopt them whenever you need to relax. The simple practice of tensing and then releasing your muscles offer an overall sense of rejuvenation that helps you to ease the tension out of your body.

1. Sit comfortably or lie down.

2. Practice deep breathing. Become mindful of how the air you inhale fills your lungs. Inhale and hold your breath to a count of four.

3. Gently release the breath and feel the tension leave your body as you breathe out.

4. Deep inhale once more and hold for a count of four.

5. Exhale gently, and as you do, imagine the tension leaving your body.

6. Focus on your feet next.

7. Curve your toes in and create inward arches with your feet. Feel how tense it is; hold the pose.

8. Gently release the tension and feel the stress leave your feet.

9. Focus on the calves of your lower legs, tense the muscles, hold it for a count of four, and release.

10. Feel the tension release.

11. Make sure to keep your breathing even throughout.

12. Now, tense the muscles in your pelvis and upper leg, hold it for four seconds, and release enjoy the sensation of release that follows.

13. Suck in your stomach, hold it for a count of four, and release.

14. Breathe in and out gently.

15. Tense your back muscles and pull your shoulders together from the back, hold for a count four, and release. Enjoy the sensation of release.

16. Make a fist, tense your lower arms, then your upper arms, and hold and release. Feel though a weight has dropped from your arms.

17. Feel the tension pour out of your fingertips, slump your shoulders and relax.

18. Now tense your whole body, feet, legs, thighs, pelvis, tummy, shoulders, and arms; hold for a count of four and release. Feel the flood of tension leave your body.

19. Now gently breathe in and out, lay still, and concentrate on your breathing as the last of your tension is trickling out of your body.

20. Close your eyes, and count to ten.

21. Now slowly activate your muscles starting from your feet.

22. Stretch.

23. Open your eyes and enjoy feeling rejuvenated.

The more you practice this exercise, the more adept you become at using it to de-stress whenever you need it.

y Journal:

)cument your experience.

_____

_____

_____

_____

_____

_____

_____

_____

_____

_____

_____

Exercise 128: Rating Your Distress, Anxiety, Anger, and Fear According to SUDS

Subjective units of distress scale or SUDS is a level on which you can measure the changes your stress levels. It's similar to the feelings thermometer and helps you to gauge how high your distress levels can climb.

SUDS Thermometer

100	Distress, fear, and anxiety are higher than any other time
90	Distress and anxiety are at an extreme
80	Quite anxious and distress is bad, lack of concentration
70	Anxiety is extreme and starts to hinder performance
60	
50	Anxiety and distress are moderate, it interferes with performance but does not stop
40	
30	Anxiety and distress are mild and will not interfere with performance
20	Anxiety and distress are at a minimum
10	Alert, awake, and able to concentrate successfully
0	Totally laid back and relaxed

My Journal:

Document your experience.

Use the SUDS Thermometer for a week to gauge how your anxiety fluctuates. Mark down every reaction according to the scale; how long the anxiety lasted and the DBT technique you use to bring down your anxiety.

Day	How High My Anxiety Started and Where it Was Last on the SUDS Thermometer	What I Was Doing at the Time and What I Did to Bring it Down
Monday		
Tuesday		
Wednesday		
Thursday		
Friday		
Saturday		
Sunday		

Exercise 129: Techniques to Stop Anger From Interfering With Your Interactions

Being mindful of how you interact with other people is mindful communication. We alre touched on this subject in the Active Listening and Communications Workbook. Now let's use technique to adopt mindfulness when communicating when experiencing anger.

The first step is to accept and focus on your feelings instead of using sentences that pass blame to the other person; use "I" instead of "you."

Examples of sentences you can use:

- "I feel annoyed when I get home and find the house is a mess."

- "I get frustrated when my feelings are not considered."

- "I feel that this problem has been going on for too long."

Steps to Healthy and Mindful Communication When Angry

1. Process Then Speak

When angry, you need a time-out before you speak to the other person. Take time to process your emotion. Are you angry, frustrated, hurt, or sad. Identify the core emotion before you lash out by latching onto anger as the feeling you are dealing with.

2. Turn Away

Do not respond to the other person immediately, especially if it's a loved one you will regret hurting. Turn away if you must. Look down, regroup your thoughts, and think about what you are about to say. Is it worth responding in a negative tone? What alternate answer can you give?

3. Write Down Your Answers

If you are arguing with your partner and you do not trust yourself to speak clearly, write down the emotions you are feeling; did you get hurt? Do you accept your faults? What are you feeling right now apart from anger? Write down your response and then return to face your partner.

. Use the 'I' Statements to Express Yourself

Avoid passing the blame by using "I feel" statements to express yourself.

. Become Mindful

Step aside and observe the situation as a stranger; change your perspective of what you think happened and who is to blame. Observe from a different angle without judging or criticizing.

. Do Not Dredge Up the Past

Do not use past incidents as ammunition. Stay in the present and address the present situation.

Become Attentive

Before you accuse, listen. Be attentive to what the other person is saying and prepare to accept it.

- Today I practiced Mindful Communication When I Was Angry:

Exercise 130: RAVEN Negotiation Skills

Using the RAVEN skills, you can achieve emotional regulation and improve your negotiation skills during a conflict. Conflict is not bad when you use negotiation skills to find a solution while being respectful to your and the other person's emotions, needs, and ideals.

RAVEN Skills
Relax: Take back your breath as it makes you aware of the conflict that is taking place. Do so by mindfully slowing down your breathing. Consciously inhale and exhale. Using the counting technique as an added tool to slow down your breathing and take charge of your emotional state.
Avoid the Negative and Aversive Fight the urge to respond in the negative. Do not give in to the volatile negative emotion and use tactics that are cheap, hurtful, and instigators for future trouble with the people you care about. Focus on being fair, and reaching a mutually agreeable solution. Avoid judging and awarding points to who is right and who is wrong.
Validate and Agree The path to an amicable solution to the conflict is validating the other person's reasons, points, and feelings. Do this even when you are close to attacking and defending your reasons. Validating the other person's cause is showing them respect, and that is the basis for resolving a conflict positively.
Examine, Look at Your Needs and Expectations Treat the other person exactly the way you expect to be treated. What do you envision as a healthy relationship? What are the give-and-take factors? Implement those values, and look at the entire relationship through an open mind understanding that you cannot expect to receive what you do not give.
Neutral Tones Matter You can follow all of the above steps, but if you do not keep your voice neutral and you

continue to project your resentment and anger through your voice, you are negating everything else because the other person is going to pick up on your tone and not the words.

Today I Used RAVEN Skills to Handle a Difficult Situation:

_____

_____

_____

_____

_____

_____

_____

_____

_____

_____

_____

_____

_____

_____

_____

_____

Exercise 131: The Anger Cycle

Here is an example of the anger cycle.

	Situation	Thoughts	
	Someone cuts in front of you in the line you have been standing for over ten minutes.	"How dare they make a fool of me." It is disrespecting me. I look foolish.	
Thoughts They must not be allowed to get away with this type of behavior.			**Feelings** Irritated, upset, angry, rage.
Behaviors Shouting, pointing, and making a fuss.			**Behaviors** Glaring at the person, talking loudly for them to hear, and being rude.

	Thoughts	Physical Symptoms	
	That person saw we were all standing in line and cut in front anyway!	Heart rate increases, face feels flushed, and body temperature rises.	

Recall a similar incident you experienced and fill in your anger cycle.

	Situation	Thoughts	
Thoughts			Feelings
Behaviors			Behaviors
	Thoughts	Physical Symptoms	

xercise 132: Anger Triggers

Each person will react to anger triggers in a different fashion. Let's look at some common iggers and the range of possible reactions you may have to them.

Triggers have deep-rooted meanings for each of us, often going back to our childhood. If you e constantly made to feel unworthy, someone disrespecting you may trigger uncontrollable nger. Use the chart to see how intense your reactions are to these common triggers.

Trigger	My Reaction (add a tick √ to the appropriate reaction)		
	Slightly annoyed	Angry	Infuriating
Disrespect			
Language that's abusive			
Blaming, shaming, labeling			
Injustice			
Disrespecting your personal space			
Insults			
Lying			
Insults			
Threatening physical violence			
Disappointments			
No control			

Misinformation			
Exclusivity, including only some			
Disputes within a relationship			

What I learned from this exercise:

_____

_____

_____

_____

_____

_____

_____

_____

_____

_____

_____

_____

_____

_____

_____

Exercise 133: Deep Slow Breathing With Positive Visualization

Deep breathing coupled with positive visualization works to help calm your parasympathetic response. Here are some tips for using this mindfulness technique to calm your anger.

1. Sit or lie down in a comfortable position, and start deep breathing.

2. Inhale deeply, and feel your belly puff out. Inhale to a count of three.

3. Hold your breath to a count of four, then gently exhale to a count of six, feeling relaxed as you do so.

4. Once more, breathe into a count of three and breathe out to a count of six.

5. As you inhale, imagine you are inhaling calmness, you are dragging that feeling deep into your body, and it's pushing out the anger. Now hold that breath and feel the emotion wash over you.

6. Breathe out to a count of six, and as you let out your breath, close your eyes and visualize your anger leaving your body as a puff of smoke that you exhale.

7. Alternatively, you can imagine breathing in the calming tones of the color blue or green and breathing out the color red.

Once done, stay for a minute or two with your eyes closed. Become conscious that the tension and anger have left your body and you are no longer experiencing the negative emotion. Smile. Breathe in and out. Open your eyes.

Exercise 134: The Anger Iceberg

Anger that is manifested as a negative emotion is just the top of the iceberg, the outwardly er. But if you look below the surface, you will realize your anger has many layers hidden below surface. Those layers are represented by different emotions: sadness, guilt, jealousy, insecurity, , etc. These alternate emotions are the root cause of your anger which really is just the final er for all the other emotions that lead to your distress.

The remedy for fixing your anger issues lies in these root emotions. If your insecurity causes anger, then you need to concentrate more on loving yourself and focusing on self-care as a to build up your self-esteem.

If fear is causing your anxiety, you must try to face the emotion to understand the type of you are dealing with. Fear of abandonment can make you suspicious, clingy, and emotionally cure leading to anger as an easy outlet for dealing with these emotions.

Think of anger as the mask of your real emotions. Your vulnerabilities: shame, hurt, guil etc., that you automatically disguise as anger. The only way to uncover these masked emotions to be true to yourself. Use a journal to hash out your emotions and why you think they surfaced

Example:

I got angry with my partner when he canceled our date because he had to work late.

- Why did I get angry? Was it because of my disappointment, or did I feel insecure? Was suspicious? Am I afraid he may abandon me?

_____

_____

_____

_____

_____

_____

_____

_____

_____

_____

_____

Paranoid thoughts can take over and influence your behavior. They, too, are rooted in in emotions that harbor your real fears and insecurities. Let's explore them in our last chapter.

Chapter NINE

The Link Between DPD and Temporary Paranoid Thought

Paranoia: the gift of the survivor and the burden of the overtired, stressed, and terrified.

- Patricia Briggs

---

aranoid thoughts are fueled by many different factors. Childhood trauma, the environment you grew up in, genetics, or simply exhaustion brought on by a lack of sleep. Substance abuse lead to dissociative episodes, similar to how hallucinations and feelings of insecurity are ignited negative emotions of anger, fear, and stress.

This chapter looks at DBT skills as well as lifestyle changes you can use to bring about change to your paranoid mindset.

Bringing the Mind Back to the Present

Dissociation episodes take place when you are stressed, traumatized, and when dealing wi mental health conditions. Triggers linked to these factors cause the condition to take place.

- Feeling of disconnection between your mind and body.

- Losing your sense of identity.

- Forgetting certain events or missing a sense of time.

These are some of the common symptoms of dissociation. The syndrome itself can diagnosed under several factors and disorders. Such as dissociative amnesia and dissociati identity disorder (DID) or multiple personality disorder; there are also unspecified dissociati disorders.

The syndrome, when triggered, causes a separation of mind and body, with the effects last for a short period (until the instigating trauma subsides) or may go on long-term, requir treatment.

Self-Care Management Skills

The grounding and mindfulness techniques presented here will help you bring your m back to the present, syncing your mind and body whenever you feel a trigger for dissociati Experiment and find the technique that offers you the best results, as each person's response to exercises is varied.

Exercise 135: Journaling

Journaling will help you to put your thoughts in one place to be viewed from a diffe perspective. It is a good technique to help you to face your fears, frustrations, and nega emotions.

Make journaling a daily habit if you find your insecurities often lead to a sense of dissociat Writing down the events that transpired will help you to create a connection with your thou and behavior once more.

ake care when journaling to avoid judgment and critical thinking that will create low self-esteem. ind a positive angle to the day's event and triggers that lead to your dissociation.

---

ercise 136: Grounding Techniques

These techniques will help you to be in the present especially if past traumas act as flashback gers for your dissociation.

Some of the techniques are those we have already discussed, and you may have begun ticing them already. Remember, the more frequently you use these techniques, the easier and e efficient they will become.

Become Aware of Your Environment

When you feel your triggers are being activated and distress taking over, step away from the tion you are in; go outside or stand at a window. Observe your surroundings, notice what's g on, what's present, trees, people, etc. Observe for five minutes, then close your eyes and try call what you saw. You can speak out loud or talk in your mind.

2. Visualize

Close your eyes and think of a place that ignites a sense of calm and peace. It can be imagine or real as long as no traumatic events are associated with the place. With your eyes closed, try ar visualize the place naming everything that makes it special.

3. Using Positive Words or Affirmations

Constantly using positive affirmations will help you deal with low self-esteem and the trauma th follows. Make a habit of repeating your favorite phrases daily as a ritual.

- When you wake up.

- When eating a meal.

- When traveling.

Try to create a pattern where you automatically repeat the phrases during a routine activi Choose phrases that are uplifting.

- "I'm strong in mind."

- "I am special, and I deserve to be respected."

- "I can conquer my fears. They are not my weakness."

- "Have courage."

- "Be strong."

4. Focus on a Favorite Object

Pick an object that sends positive vibes through your body. Something that is linked to happy productive memories. Use this object as a grounding tool to help you calm down when y triggers are activated.

_____

_____

_____

_____

Mindfulness Meditation the Band of Light

This exercise helps you to focus fully on what is taking place in the present. It makes you aware of your physical self, putting you in touch with your body and the sensations you are feeling at the moment.

Exercise 137: The Band of Light Technique for Mindfulness

Choose a quiet, serene spot, someplace where you will not be disturbed. Sit comfortably and close your eyes.

Begin deep breathing, and continue for about one or two minutes.

Now with your eyes closed and as you continue to breathe, visualize a band of white light circling the top of your head.

Become aware of physical sensations where you envision the light to be circling; tingling, or itching of the scalp; it does not have to be a specific sensation.

Do you feel muscle tension in your head?

Imagine the band of white light floating down your head, over your eyes, nose, ears, mouth, and chin.

Remain sensitive to the physical sensation you are feeling.

You may feel the most sensations in the back of your head.

Do you have a strange sensation in your mouth, tongue, or lips?

Imagine the band of light floating down your neck.

Become aware of muscle tensions you may feel at the back of your neck and sensations in your throat.

- The band has expanded and is now moving down your shoulder, continuing to breathe in and out.

- If your mind wanders, bring it back.

- As the band of light descends your torso, notice, and sensations of tingling, muscle tension you will feel in your upper back, lower back, arms, stomach, and chest.

- The same sensations are taking over your buttocks, thighs and lower legs as the band continues to descend. It is now at your feet; they are tingling. And slowly, the band leaves your body and disappears.

- Continue to deep breathe with your eyes closed for a minute.

- Slowly open your eyes, look around the room, and bring your focus back.

Document your experience.

_____

_____

_____

_____

_____

_____

_____

_____

_____

_____

_____

xercise 138: Mindfulness Bell Technique

his exercise will help you to remain grounded and focused on what is taking place now. ownload a video with the sound of a single and deep bell sound. It should be one that rings and en echoes as it fades away.

- Sit with your eyes closed, and deep breathe.

- Play the bell video.

- Listen intently and focus entirely on the sound of the bell, hear its vibration.

- Listen until the noise fades away into the distance.

    You can repeat the exercise several times until you feel your focus is entirely on the sound of ᵉ bell.

ᵓcument your experience.

_____

_____

_____

_____

_____

_____

_____

_____

_____

_____

Stopping Dissociative Episodes Before They Escalate

Psychosis may set you apart from the average person. Seeing and hearing things others don Strange and unpredictable behavior and struggling to complete basic daily tasks like studying taking care of your needs, and working are all symptoms of psychosis.

What Keeps Psychosis Going?

Your Beliefs, Past, and Assumptions		Interpretation of Triggers in Threatening or Unusual Ways
If you are dealing with psychosis, you will harbor special beliefs. They would have formed through a traumatic event or may have been triggered as a self-preservation mechanism. They include beliefs and thoughts such as; • "People try to hurt me on purpose." • "I am very special." • "I am sensitive and vulnerable." • "I'm easily hurt." These beliefs are often created to compensate for traumatic experiences you may have encountered. Therefore the beliefs are	**W** **H** **A** **T** **K** **E** **E** **P** **S**	A main feature of psychosis is thoughts and ideals that are not normal. You will interpret things in extremes that make you and those you love seem unsafe. You may behave in ways that you believe are needed to keep you safe but in fact, cause more trauma. You will have a sudden thought and then believe it was not yours. You do not live a life that is emotionally and mentally free.

put in place to help you feel:

- Safe

- Safeguard your emotions

- Help you to make sense of the world and what's happening in your life.

↱↵

P
S
Y
C
H
O
S
I
S

G
O
I
N
G

Attention Biases and Strategies to Control Thoughts

Dealing with psychosis will cause you to try to manage your thoughts. But in a bid to gain control, you may end up focusing on negative and threatening aspects rather than the positive.

Despite you implementing them as a safeguard, these policies can cause harm and prevent from discovering what truly is taking place.

↱↵

Safety Behaviors and Avoidance

You may end up avoiding situations because you're paranoid thoughts are making you feel unsafe.

You will try to control what's happening in your surroundings and hide from situations you feel are unsafe.

This behavior leads to problems and prevents you from gauging what the situation is really about.

Exercise 139: My Mind Map for Dealing With Psychosis

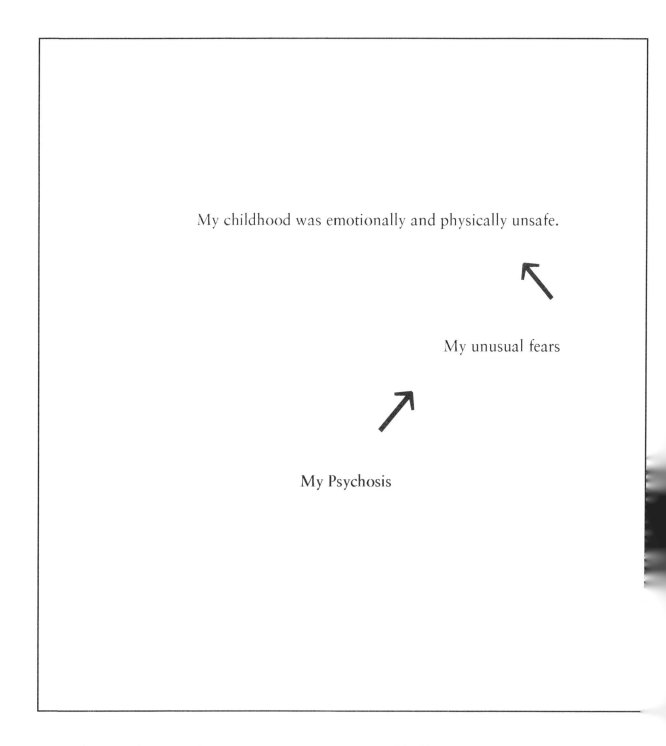

Use this mind map to brainstorm your paranoia and hallucinations.

The first "my unusual fears" is done as an example; try to create links to each block you backtrack and arrive at the root cause of your psychosis.

My Notes on What I Discovered About My Psychosis:

Exercise 140: Coping Affirmations for Dealing With a Difficult Situation

Sometimes we need encouragement to tell us what is transpiring is not the end of the world. In those moments, it's good to draw inspiration from what we have been telling ourselves. The affirmations can help you to deal with a difficult situation before your feelings of overwhelm overshadow your rational thought. Learn to change your thoughts and beliefs with these positive affirmations.

- "I am not damaged, I am worthy of the person I am."

- "I can face my fears without running away."

- "I do not deserve to be in this situation, I can change it."

- "I am stronger than I feel right now."

- "Who I am is enough for me to get by."

- "I am worthy of love."

- "It's okay to be afraid, but I can also be courageous."

- "I will take care of my needs."

- "My negative feelings will pass."

- "There is a lot I can be thankful for."

- "I am going to be optimistic."

- "I can focus on the present, it's okay to take one day at a time."

Choose the affirmations that resonate with you the most and repeat them as a daily practice.

PLEASE MASTER Technique for Taking Care of Your Needs

Our impulsive and emotional behavior often stems from a lack of self-care. Failing to care of our needs leaves us vulnerable to negative emotions. Dealing with stress, extreme fatigue and even hunger are triggers for losing control.

PLEASE MASTER skills are aimed at teaching you self-care techniques that help to foster balanced and positive thoughts and behavior.

xercise 141: PLEASE MASTER Skills

et's break down the acronym to help you cope and take care of yourself.

P + L = Treat Physical Illness

This is to remind you that taking care of your medical and health needs is important. Your daily pills, keeping your doctors' appointments, maintaining your scheduled checkups, etc., that need to be met as part of maintaining a healthy lifestyle is important.

E= Balanced Eating

It's important to eat a balanced meal to maintain a healthy outlook. Striving to increase the number of nutrient-dense meals as opposed to calorie-dense meals will help you to stay fit and strong.

A= Avoid Mood-Altering Drugs and Substances

Avoid dependence on drugs, alcohol, and medication that can alter your moods. You lose part of your resolve to stay on the path and stick to your principles when you are under the influence of substances that control your mind.

S= Balanced Sleep

Getting adequate sleep is crucial for a healthy mind and body. A lack of sleep can lead to fatigue which can lead to rash decisions and a lack of control over your negative emotions. A rested mind and body are alert, sharp, and capable of handling challenges.

E=Exercise

Physical exertion is just as important as sleep. It provides a healthy outlet for your mind and body to function at their best. Physical exertion triggers the release of endorphins and neurochemicals, which are your feel-good hormones.

M=Mastery

This is to remind you to indulge in activities that bring you pleasure and make you happy. Engaging in activities that you are good at will feed your sense of accomplishment and bring you satisfaction and joy.

My Notes on Using the PLEASE MASTERY Skill:

_____

_____

_____

_____

_____

_____

_____

_____

_____

_____

_____

_____

_____

_____

_____

_____

_____

————◆————

Building Mastery Skills for Improving Self-Esteem

A lack of self-esteem can hold you back from trying new things and reaching your potential. What you harbor then is a negative mindset; therefore, the building mastery becomes a valuable DBT tool for helping you gain self-esteem and confidence to flip your thin over to the positive.

Practicing this skill will help you to change an "I don't think I am the suitable person for promotion" to "I am going to aim for the promotion and get it!"

xercise 142: Practicing Building Mastery Skills

Building Mastery One Step at a Time
1. Build mastery daily by indulging in just one thing you like. Allocate just ten minutes toward the activity to feel happy and satisfied.
2. Start small and aim for success. Choose to indulge in activities that you can handle and succeed. Don't attempt to swim 30 laps in one go on your first try, build your stamina and then work to increase the number of laps, and before long, you will be breezing through the laps and taking part in that long-distance swim challenge
3. Increase the level of difficulty gradually. To feel confident and good about yourself, you must indulge in challenging tasks. Therefore, gradually increasing the difficulty ratio in the tasks you undertake will instill a sense of satisfaction in you. For example, if your aim is to build up your physique, you can gradually increase your workout to include weights as well.
4. Take on a challenge. Set your aim high and strive to reach your best potential. Even when you think all odds are against you, counter those negative thoughts with positive ones and tell yourself you will reach your goals. For example, if you never earned your college degree, you can always go back to night school and earn it. It may not be easy with your responsibilities and duties as an adult, but if you are determined enough, you can find the will to study and reach that goal.

w I Used Building Mastery Skills to Improve My Negative Thoughts.

_____

_____

_____

_____

_____

Exercise 143: The ABC Technique

The ABC technique is used in rational emotional behavioral therapy (REBT), where t[...] connection between thoughts, emotions, and behavior are explained. Follow the ABC chart to h[...] control your thoughts and behavior according to the specifics of the model.

A = Activating Event
Something takes place in the
environment surrounding you, or
something happens to you.

B=Belief
Your preconceived
understanding/belief of
the activating event
that took place.

C=Consequences
That preconceived belief you possess
comes with consequences and is reflected
in emotions and behavior.

D=Disputation Challenge your beliefs; could they be wrong? Can you add new beliefs that are more appropriate to the activating event?

E= Effective You can find new beliefs that are more effective for dealing with the activating belief.

activating event today was:

_____

_____

ed the ABC technique to successfully change my beliefs to ideals that helped solve the event in appropriate manner.

_____

_____

_____

_____

———◆———

Preventing Paranoid Thoughts By Keeping a Check on Your Emotions

Those dealing with depression or PTSD commonly deal with paranoid intrusive negat thoughts. Intrusive thoughts are common among people dealing with neurodegenera conditions, but did you know that through the use and practice of the appropriate DBT skill, can learn to control your emotions and keep your paranoid thoughts in check?

Exercise 144: The Intrusive Memory Record

Intrusive memories take place automatically; they are those random unproductive thou that pop into your head involuntarily. They are often triggered by paranoia but for an accu record of what those thoughts are and what triggers them, you can use the intrusive mem record.

Step 1: Write down the moment an intrusive paranoid memory takes place.

Step 2: Write down the stimuli that caused it or the trigger that instigated the memory.

Step 3: Record all the details of the memory. What it was, where it took place, and what sen unit you are able to associate with the memory; smell, touch, sight, taste, or sound.

Step 4: Rate how recent the memory is. How close is the déjà vu feeling of that memory as th it is happening again right now?

Step 5: On a scale of 1–10, rate how much the distress was associated with that memory.

Date & Time	My Intrusive Thought	Trigger That Caused It	What It Was About	How Distressing It Was On a Scale of 1–10

Exercise 145: Challenging Paranoid Thoughts

This worksheet will help you to reevaluate your challenging thoughts by addressing the once more from a fresh new perspective. Before you answer each of the questions, spend tir reflecting on the answer.

Irrational thoughts based on negative beliefs and low self-esteem often lead to mental hea conditions like depression and anxiety. Also, paranoid or irrational thoughts make it tough enjoy your positive outcomes. For example, let's say you worked hard on a presentation at wo and your boss loved it, but he points out one element that could do even better with a f enhancements; you take this mild criticism in a negative light and go on to think you were a failu and your boss hates all the work you did. Do you see how that one negative and intrusive thoug turned everything else topsy-turvy?

This chart will help you to stop falling victim to such paranoid thoughts. Write your answ in the space provided.

1. How valid is this thought I am dealing with? Is there enough evidence to prove it's correct?

Document your experience.

2. Are there factors that contradict my thoughts to prove that I may be wrong?

Document your experience.

3. Am I being too quick to judge this event? Do I have enough evidence to prove my thoughts are justified?

Document your experience.

_____

_____

_____

_____

_____

_____

_____

_____

_____

_____

_____

4. If my friend were faced with this situation, how would they handle it? What would they think?

Document your experience.

_____

_____

_____

_____

5. If I stopped being negative and changed the way I look at the situation to judge it in a positive light, would it turn out to be different?

Document your experience.

6. Is this such a huge problem? One year from now, will it still have an impact? What about five years from now, can it impact me?

Document your experience.

Exercise 145: More Grounding Skills

Staying in the present is important to avoid dissociation and focus on avoiding paranoid thoughts. Therefore as our last exercise, let's look at a few more grounding techniques that will help bring you back into focus and the present moment.

- Walk on the beach barefoot and feel the sand crunch beneath your feet as they sink into the soft warmth of the sand.

- Watch a movie that makes you laugh, even if it is a re-run.

- Eat something that's spicy or sour and activates your tastebuds.

- Make a list of all your favorite things.

Document your experience.

_____

_____

_____

_____

_____

_____

_____

_____

_____

_____

_____

Build a Sensory Kit

This can be a bag or even a box into which you put important items. They should igni[te] positive memories in you and include items that stimulate your senses; water beads, pieces of puzzle, water feathers, beans, dry chickpeas, bits of plastic, etc., are added to give you a senso[ry] experience.

Reach Out

Remember that the best tool to deal with paranoia is the company and the help of anot[her] person. Therefore, do not be afraid to reach out to a friend, family member, community memb[er] and so on, anyone you trust when you feel you need help.

Keep practicing the skills in this book, and in time you will learn to use them accurately a[nd] anywhere when you need that additional aid for dealing with your sudden and erratic bursts [of] panic and distress.

Help the Author & Readers

Leave a Rating and Review

I would be incredibly thankful if you could take 60 seconds to write a brief review on Amazon, even if it's just a few sentences.

1 Click Review

http://amazon.com/review/create-review

Self Help Checklist

Self Help Checklist

Chapter	Topic	Weeks	Completed (Y /N)
0	General DBT Skill	1	
1	Skills to Overcome Fear of Abandonment	2	
2	Establish Healthy Relationships Skills	3	
3	Build Self-Esteem Skills	4	
4	Coping With Moods Skills	5	
5	Control Impulsive Behavior	6	
6	Protecting Yourself From Self-Harm	7	
7	Finding Fulfillment With Mindfulness	8	
8	Manage Anger	9	
9	Bringing the Mind Back to the Present	10	
9	Self-Care Management Skills	11	
9	Stopping Dissociative Episodes	12	

Conclusion

You are now equipped with a variety of skills and tools that can help you overcome the conditions, syndromes, and negative habits associated with BPD. Strive to lead a life that is free from distressing thoughts and emotions by using the skills in this book to overcome your emotional dysfunctions. Learn from your past mistakes and never fail to look at every problem with a new perspective.

Doing so will not be difficult as you use the four main skills of DBT to heal. Let's recall them.

Distress tolerance techniques

Mindfulness

Emotional regulation skills

Strengthening interpersonal relationships

Use the techniques here to settle down and look forward to a happier and fulfilling love that not encumbered by unruly and unwelcome thoughts, memories, and behavior.

Get in Touch

We would love to hear from you as part of our service to the community. Those of us dealing BPD are looked at negatively, which helps us to bring about a change and show BPD as a gnized dysfunctional emotional habit that can be cured through patience, understanding, and .

Leave your review and help us spread the word about BPD and the DBT skills that can help e diagnosed to move on and enjoy a normal lifestyle.

info@dbtorcbt.com

Christopher Edward & Naziah Idrees also wrote the book below

A Practical DBT Skills Workbook
For
Modern Teens and Adolescents

101 Highly Effective Activities and Step-By-Step Techniques

How to Help You Confront Your Emotions and Anxiety, Keep Them Under Control, and Practice Mindfulness

By

Christopher B. K. Edward & Naziah Idrees, PhD

A PRACTICAL
DBT SKILLS WORKBOOK
(DIALECTICAL BEHAVIORAL THERAPY)
FOR
MODERN TEENS
AND ADOLESCENTS

101 Highly Effective Activities
and Step-By-Step Techniques

How To Help You Confront Your Emotions
and Anxiety, Keep Them Under Control,
and Practice Mindfulness

Christopher B. K. Edward & Naziah Idrees, PhD

Christopher Edward & Naziah Idrees also wrote the book below

A Practical DBT Skills Workbook for Radically Eliminating Neurodivergent Disorders

Help You Confront Your Social Anxiety Triggers

Improve Your Sensory Processing

Improve Your Interpersonal Effectiveness, Social Skills

Reclaim Your Life

By

Christopher B. K. Edward & Nazish Idrees, PhD

A PRACTICAL
DBT WORKBOOK
—— F O R ——
RADICALLY ELIMINATING
NEURODIVERGENT
DISORDERS

113 Highly Effective Activities and Step-By-Step Techniques

✓ Help You Confront Your Social Anxiety Triggers
✓ Improve Your Sensory Processing
✓ Improve Your Interpersonal Effectiveness, and Social Skills
✓ Reclaim Your Life

Christopher B. K. Edward & Nazish Idrees , PhD

Glossary

- **Cognitive skills:** The main skills your brain taps into to help your sense, in other words, your ability to reason, read, learn, think and pay attention.

- **Detrimental:** An undesirable or even harmful person or thing. (Websters)

- **Emotional dysregulation:** Unable to take control of their thoughts and behavior.

- **Neurodivergent:** Having a difference in brain functions and includes several variations.

- **Pseudo:** Untrue version of something. It can be ten or ten years old. (Websters)

References

kerman, Courtney. "22 Mindfulness Exercises, Techniques & Activities for Adults (+ PDF's)." *PositivePsychology.com*, 18 Jan. 2017, positivepsychology.com/mindfulness-exercises-techniques-activities/.

kerman, Courtney E. "18 Self-Esteem Worksheets and Activities for Teens and Adults (+PDFs)." *PositivePsychology.com*, 19 June 2019, positivepsychology.com/self-esteem-worksheets/.

Haddad, Hani, et al. "Influence of Cold Water Face Immersion on Post-Exercise Parasympathetic Reactivation." *European Journal of Applied Physiology*, vol. 108, no. 3, 31 Oct. 2009, pp. 599–606, 10.1007/s00421-009-1253-9. Accessed 24 Aug. 2019.

ertive Communication. *Assertive Communication Worksheet*.

tistin, Jennie M. "5,4,3,2,1 Method to Reduce Anxiety." *Hope Therapy Center*, 6 Apr. 2016, www.hope-therapy-center.com/single-post/2016/04/06/54321-method-to-reduce-anxiety.

uty Borderline. "Distress Tolerance: Pros & Cons." *Beauty and the Borderline*, 19 Mar. 2015, beautyandtheborderline.wordpress.com/2015/03/19/distress-tolerance-pros-cons/. Accessed 29 Nov. 2022.

, Nicole Nathan. "Try These Exercises That Activate the Vagus Nerve." *Goodnet*, 26 Oct. 2021, www.goodnet.org/articles/try-these-exercises-that-activate-vagus-nerve. Accessed 17 Nov. 2022.

er Help. "Most Recommended Mindfulness Exercises | BetterHelp." *Www.betterhelp.com*, 27 Oct. 2022, www.betterhelp.com/advice/general/most-recommended-mindfulness-exercises/. Accessed 30 Nov. 2022.

1. "5 Best Setting Boundaries Exercises PDF." *Coaching Online*, 5 June 2020, www.coaching-online.org/5-best-setting-boundaries-exercises-pdf/.

Boswell, Catherine. "How to Stop Feeling Empty." *WikiHow*, 6 May 2021, www.wikihow.com/Stop-Feeling-Empty.

Bregman, Greg. "Nine Practices to Help You Say No." *Harvard Business Review*, 15 Feb. 2013 hbr.org/2013/02/nine-practices-to-help-you-say.html.

Briggs, Patricia. "Patricia Briggs Quote." *A-Z Quotes*, www.azquotes.com/quote/508173?ref=paranoia. Accessed 6 Dec. 2022.

Casablanca, Sandra Silva, and Margarita Tartakovsky. "ADHD Impulse Control: 5 Strategies Tame Your Impulsive Behavior." *Psych Central*, 1 Mar. 2021, psychcentral.com/adhd/adhd-in-adults-5-tips-for-taming-impulsivity#whats-impulsive-behavior. Accessed 29 Nov. 2022.

Center Vision. *Impulse Control Melt of Freeze*. 2018, media.centervention.com/pdf/Melt-or-Freeze-Impulse-Control-Worksheet.pdf.

Chang, Kayla. "DBT Skills for Self-Harm: Distress Tolerance." *Www.healthyplace.com*, 5 Jun 2019, www.healthyplace.com/blogs/speakingoutaboutselfinjury/2019/6/distress-toleran learn-a-dbt-skill-that-curbs-self-harm. Accessed 30 Nov. 2022.

Change to Chill. "What Is Mindful Walking?" *Change to Chill*, www.changetochill.org/stay-grounded-with-mindful-walking/.

Chapman, Jennifer, et al. "Borderline Personality Disorder." *Nih.gov*, StatPearls Publishing, 2019, www.ncbi.nlm.nih.gov/books/NBK430883/.

Chowdhury, Madhuleena Roy. "What Is Emotion Regulation? + 6 Emotional Skills and Strategies." *PositivePsychology.com*, 13 Aug. 2019, positivepsychology.com/emotion-regulation/#regulation.

Cleveland Clinic. "5 Ways to Stimulate Your Vagus Nerve." *Cleveland Clinic*, 10 Mar. 2022. health.clevelandclinic.org/vagus-nerve-stimulation/.

Community, Shutterfly. "120+ I Love You Quotes: Famous Love Quotes for All | Shutterfly." *Ideas & Inspiration*, 11 Jan. 2021, www.shutterfly.com/ideas/i-love-you-quotes/.

DBT Center. "3 Mindfulness Tools for When You Want to Self-Harm - Los Angeles, CA." *L Center of the South Bay*, 20 July 2021, www.dbtcentersouthbay.com/3-mindfulness-to for-self-harm/.

DBT Therapy. "Describe Your Emotions." *DBT*, dialecticalbehaviortherapy.com/mindfulness/describe-your-emotions/.

ellasanta, Jennifer. "3 Mindfulness Exercises for Depression and Anxiety." *Blog.thetransitionhouse.org*, blog.thetransitionhouse.org/3-mindfulness-exercises-for-depression-and-anxiety.

ialectical Behavior Therapy. "4 Strategies to Cope When Your Distress Is Unbearable." *CBT Psychology*, 2 Oct. 2015, cbtpsychology.com/tolerate-distress/.

RESISTT Technique." *DBT*, dialecticalbehaviortherapy.com/distress-tolerance/resistt/.

is, Robert J., and Julian F. Thayer. "Music and Autonomic Nervous System (Dys)Function." *Music Perception*, vol. 27, no. 4, Apr. 2010, pp. 317–326, www.ncbi.nlm.nih.gov/pmc/articles/PMC3011183/, 10.1525/mp.2010.27.4.317.

ich, Sam Dylan, and Sam Dylan Finch. "9 Affirmations You Deserve to Receive If You Have a Mental Illness." *Everyday Feminism*, 10 Aug. 2015, everydayfeminism.com/2015/08/affirmations-mental-illness/. Accessed 6 Dec. 2022.

rleo, Marie. "How to Use Journaling to Find Your Purpose in Life." *The Journal Life*, 17 Oct. 2020, www.thejournallife.co.uk/blog/use-journaling-to-find-your-purpose-in-life. Accessed 4 Dec. 2022.

son, Melissa. "DBT 101: "PLEASE MASTER" & the Importance of Self-Care." *Columbus Park*, 29 May 2018, columbuspark.com/2018/05/29/dbt-101-please-master-the-importance-of-self-care/. Accessed 6 Dec. 2022.

dsmith, Barton. "10 Steps to Emotional Fulfillment | Psychology Today." *Www.psychologytoday.com*, 13 Apr. 2012, www.psychologytoday.com/us/blog/emotional-fitness/201204/10-steps-emotional-fulfillment. Accessed 4 Dec. 2022.

ssman, Amanda L. "How to Teach Delayed Gratification (Exercises for Self Control)." *Money Prodigy*, 11 Feb. 2019, www.moneyprodigy.com/how-to-teach-delayed-gratification/. Accessed 30 Nov. 2022.

lén Botella, Verónica, et al. "Exploring the Effectiveness of Dialectical Behavior Therapy versus Systems Training for Emotional Predictability and Problem Solving in a Sample of Patients with Borderline Personality Disorder." *Journal of Personality Disorders*, 6 Apr. 2020, pp. 1–18, 10.1521/pedi_2020_34_477. Accessed 2 July 2020.

man, Jennifer. "How to Be Emotionally Independent (with Pictures)." *WikiHow*, 27 Oct. 2021, www.wikihow.com/Be-Emotionally-Independent. Accessed 4 Dec. 2022.

es, Seena. "Become an ANT-Eater." *Wellbeing Elixir*, 28 Feb. 2021, wellbeingelixir.com/ant_eater/. Accessed 28 Nov. 2022.

Harmer, Bonnie, et al. "Suicidal Ideation." *PubMed*, StatPearls Publishing, 2021, pubmed.ncbi.nlm.nih.gov/33351435/.

Health Wise. "Emotional Freedom Technique (EFT) | Kaiser Permanente." *Healthy.kaiserpermanente.org*, healthy.kaiserpermanente.org/health-wellness/health-encyclopedia/he.emotional-freedom-technique-eft.acl9225.

Ho, Judy. *Stop Self Sabotage*. 2019.

Hoffman, Theressa. "Press Pause for Better Impulse Control and Better Results!" *Thrive Leadership*, 2014, thriveleadership.com/blog/2019/8/30/press-pause-for-better-impulse-control-and-better-results. Accessed 30 Nov. 2022.

Howland, Robert H. "Vagus Nerve Stimulation." *Current Behavioral Neuroscience Reports*, v 1, no. 2, 7 Mar. 2014, pp. 64–73, www.ncbi.nlm.nih.gov/pmc/articles/PMC4017164/, 10.1007/s40473-014-0010-5.

https://www.facebook.com/verywell. "How Can Dialectical Behavior Therapy for BPD Help You?" *Verywell Mind*, 2018, www.verywellmind.com/dialectical-behavior-therapy-dbt for-bpd-425454.

Inbaraj, Ganagarajan, et al. "Immediate Effects of OM Chanting on Heart Rate Variability Measures Compared between Experienced and Inexperienced Yoga Practitioners." *International Journal of Yoga*, vol. 15, no. 1, 1 Jan. 2022, pp. 52–58, pubmed.ncbi.nlm.nih.gov/35444369/, 10.4103/ijoy.ijoy_141_21. Accessed 18 Nov. 20

JED Foundation. "Practice Emotional Awareness." *The Jed Foundation*, jedfoundation.org/se to-go/practice-emotional-awareness/. Accessed 29 Nov. 2022.

Jefferson, Thomas. "Thomas Jefferson Quotes." *BrainyQuote*, www.brainyquote.com/quotes/thomas_jefferson_132201.

Johnson, R. Skip. "A 3 Minute Lesson on Ending Conflict." *Borderline Personality Disorder*, Jan. 2021, www.bpdfamily.com/content/ending-conflict. Accessed 30 Nov. 2022.

"Setting Boundaries and Setting Limits." *Borderline Personality Disorder*, 10 June 2020, www.bpdfamily.com/content/setting-boundaries. Accessed 20 Nov. 2022.

Jones, Suzanne. "The Hurt Yourself Less Workbook." *Mental Health Practice*, vol. 2, no. 6, Mar. 1999, pp. 27–27, www.studymore.org.uk/hylw.pdf, 10.7748/mhp.2.6.27.s20.

Joyner, Lisa. "4 Ways to Practice Cold Water Therapy at Home (and What We Thought Wh We Tried It)." *Country Living*, 26 June 2022, www.countryliving.com/uk/wellbeing/a40214456/cold-water-therapy-home/. Accessed Nov. 2022.

ngmann, Manuela, et al. "Effects of Cold Stimulation on Cardiac-Vagal Activation in Healthy Participants: Randomized Controlled Trial." *JMIR Formative Research*, vol. 2, no. 2, 9 Oct. 2018, www.ncbi.nlm.nih.gov/pmc/articles/PMC6334714/, 10.2196/10257.

ane, Ryan. "The Raisin Exercise for Mindfulness | Mindfulness Box." *Mindfulness Box*, 21 Feb. 2022, mindfulnessbox.com/raisin-mindfulness-exercise/.

lly, David. "The Psychology of Color — Blue." *Medium*, 12 Feb. 2019, medium.com/@davidkellyuph/the-psychology-of-color-blue-5da101e1306c.

ein, Yael. "What Is Radical Acceptance and How Can It Help Me?" *Evolve Treatment Centers*, 13 May 2021, evolvetreatment.com/blog/radical-acceptance/. Accessed 30 Nov. 2022.

owles, Amanda. "Active Listening: Communication Skill Worksheet - Mental Health Worksheets." *Mentalhealthworksheets.com*, 14 Nov. 2020, mentalhealthworksheets.com/active-listening-communication-skill-worksheet/. Accessed 27 Nov. 2022.

motion Regulation Skills: PLEASE Worksheet - Mental Health Worksheets." *Mentalhealthworksheets.com*, 19 Nov. 2020, mentalhealthworksheets.com/emotion-regulation-skills-please-worksheet/. Accessed 20 Nov. 2022.

eside Link. "Do You Know Your Anger Triggers?" *Lakeside*, 1 Mar. 2011, lakesidelink.com/blog/do-you-know-your-anger-triggers/.

ley University. "Perception Is Reality: The Looking-Glass Self." *Lesley University*, 2019, lesley.edu/article/perception-is-reality-the-looking-glass-self.

in, Nancy. "How Your Fears Prevent You from Setting Boundaries." *Nancy Levin*, 11 June 2019, nancylevin.com/how-your-fears-prevent-you-from-setting-boundaries/.

ehan, Marsha M. *EMOTION REGULATION HANDOUT 1 Goals of Emotion Regulation UNDERSTAND and NAME YOUR OWN EMOTIONS Identify (Observe and Describe) Your Emotions. DECREASE the FREQUENCY of UNWANTED EMOTIONS DECREASE EMOTIONAL VULNERABILITY DECREASE EMOTIONAL SUFFERING.* 2015.

han, Masha M. *Interpersonal Effectiveness Handouts Handouts for Goals and Factors That Interfere.* 2015.

ley, Diane. "Guided Meditation for Healthy Relationships - 15 Minutes." *Www.youtube.com*, 2022, www.youtube.com/watch?v=Aho7Tsya8BI. Accessed 22 Nov. 2022.

LPC, Laura K. Schenck, Ph D. "How to Negotiate Using R-A-V-E-N - Mindfulness Muse." *Mindfulness Muse*, 19 May 2011, www.mindfulnessmuse.com/dialectical-behavior-therapy/how-to-negotiate-using-r-a-v-e-n. Accessed 5 Dec. 2022.

MA, Courtney E. Ackerman. "21 Mindfulness Exercises & Activities for Adults (+ PDF)." *PositivePsychology.com*, 18 Jan. 2017, positivepsychology.com/mindfulness-exercises-techniques-activities/#mindfulness-exercises-DBT. Accessed 6 Dec. 2022.

Mairanz, Alyssa. "Improve Self-Esteem and Confidence by Building Mastery." *Empower Your Mind Therapy*, 18 Sept. 2017, eymtherapy.com/blog/improve-self-esteem-and-confidence-by-building-mastery/.

Marchenko, Anna. "How to Stop Overthinking in a Relationship." *Up Journey*, The Editors, 8 Sept. 2021, www.datingscout.com/b6/image/upload/ds/upload/press/US1/coverage/2021/2021-09-0 upjourney-how-to-stop-overthinking-in-a-relationship.pdf. Accessed Nov. 2022.

Martin, Sharon. "Affirmations for Difficult Times." *Psych Central*, 19 Mar. 2020, psychcentral.com/blog/imperfect/2020/03/affirmations-for-difficult-times#Affirmations-for-stress-and-anxiety. Accessed 6 Dec. 2022.

Matsubayashi, Tetsuya, et al. "Does the Installation of Blue Lights on Train Platforms Shift Suicide to Another Station?: Evidence from Japan." *Journal of Affective Disorders*, vol. 169, Dec. 2014, pp. 57–60, 10.1016/j.jad.2014.07.036.

McGill Counseling. *Self Help for Anger.*

Mind Matters. "What Are Cognitive Skills?" *Mind Matters*, 2018, www.mindmattersjo.com/what-are-cognitive-skills.html.

Mindfulness Exercises. "Three Mindfulness Exercises for Anger." *Mindfulness Exercises*, 13 2015, mindfulnessexercises.com/three-mindfulness-exercises-anger/.

Mindset Worksheet.

Mrs Merry. "Feelings Thermometer Worksheet." *Mrs. Merry*, shop.mrsmerry.com/products/feelings-thermometer-worksheet. Accessed 5 Dec. 2022.

My Personal Beliefs Worksheet. *My Personal Beliefs.*

NAMI. "Borderline Personality Disorder | NAMI: National Alliance on Mental Illness." *Nami.org*, Dec. 2017, www.nami.org/About-Mental-Illness/Mental-Health-Conditions/Borderline-Personality-Disorder.

askar, Abhijit. "Recklessness Quotes (34 Quotes)." *Www.goodreads.com*, www.goodreads.com/quotes/tag/recklessness.

etwork, Allegheny Health. "Distress Tolerance: Techniques to Interrupt Extreme Emotions." *My Wish for Moms*, 30 Apr. 2020, mywishformoms.org/2654/distress-tolerance-four-tips-to-interrupt-mood-swings/. Accessed 28 Nov. 2022.

ptimistic Minds. "Borderline Personality Disorder Self Help Worksheets (5) | OptimistMinds." *Optimistminds.com*, 13 Mar. 2020, optimistminds.com/borderline-personality-disorder-self-help-worksheets/. Accessed 29 Nov. 2022.

tessa Moshfegh. "Mood Swings Quotes (25 Quotes)." *Www.goodreads.com*, www.goodreads.com/quotes/tag/mood-swings. Accessed 28 Nov. 2022.

ntazi, Joanna. "The 12 Blocks to Active Listening." *Youniversetherapy*, 19 Nov. 2018, www.youniversetherapy.com/post/the-12-blocks-to-active-listening.

pe, Karla. "50 Self-Love Quotes to Boost Your Confidence and Lift Your Spirits." *Good Housekeeping*, 23 Nov. 2021, www.goodhousekeeping.com/life/g38333580/self-love-quotes/.

itive Affirmations. "Positive Affirmations - Borderline Support UK CIC." *Borderline Support*, 21 Aug. 2021, borderlinesupport.org.uk/recovery/positiveaffirmations/?qp=3. Accessed 27 Nov. 2022.

itive Psychology. *Radical Acceptance Worksheet.*

chology Tools. "What Keeps Psychosis Going?" *Psychology Tools*, www.psychologytools.com/resource/what-keeps-psychosis-going/. Accessed 6 Dec. 2022.

chology tools. "Intrusive Memory Record." *Psychology Tools*, www.psychologytools.com/resource/intrusive-memory-record/. Accessed 6 Dec. 2022.

ing People First in Mental Health. "Borderline Personality Disorder: What You Need to Know | McLean Hospital." *Www.mcleanhospital.org*, www.mcleanhospital.org/essential/bpd.

te Master. "When I Tried to Imagine Being Beautiful, I Could Only Imagine Living without the Perpetual Fear of Being Alone, without the Great Burden of Isolation, Which Is What Feeling Ugly Felt Like. Lucy Grealy." *Www.quotemaster.org*, www.quotemaster.org/qafe231097f6f584413094cb95350b34b. Accessed 13 Oct. 2022.

el, Crystal. "Affirmations for Anxiety: How to Make and Use Them." *Healthline*, 24 June 2020, www.healthline.com/health/mental-health/affirmations-for-anxiety#creating-them.

Rather, Jill H, and Alec L Miller. *Emotional Regulation Skills ✱ ABC PLEASE Overview How Increase Positive Emotions and Reduce Vulnerability to Emotional Mind.*

The Recovery Village. "8 Tips for Overcoming Symptoms of Impulse Control Disorder & Finding Treatment." *The Recovery Village Drug and Alcohol Rehab*, 26 May 2022, www.therecoveryvillage.com/mental-health/impulse-control-disorder/how-to-overcome-impulse-control-disorder/. Accessed 30 Nov. 2022.

Red Bubble. "Mood Meter Poster by Monikapeters4." *Redbubble*, www.redbubble.com/i/poster/Mood-Meter-by-monikapeters4/75924965.LVTDI#&gid=1&pid=2. Accessed 28 Nov. 2022.

Rethink Mental Illness. "What Is Dissociation and Dissociative Identity Disorder (DID)?" *What Are the Signs and Symptoms of Dissociation and Dissociative Disorder?*, 2019, www.rethink.org/advice-and-information/about-mental-illness/learn-more-about-conditions/dissociation-and-dissociative-identity-disorder-did/.

Ridge, Tamara. "Distress Tolerance - Essential for Successful Couples' Therapy." *The Center Healthy Relationships*, 22 Mar. 2018, centerforhealthyrelationshipsla.org/advice/distress-tolerance-essential-for-successful-couples-therapy/. Accessed 25 Nov. 2022.

Schopenhauer, Arthur. "Arthur Schopenhauer Quotes." *BrainyQuote*, www.brainyquote.com/quotes/arthur_schopenhauer_155445?src=t_boredom. Accessed 30 Nov. 2022.

Skyland Trail. "Survive a Crisis Situation with DBT Distress Tolerance Skills." *Skyland Trail*, Aug. 2019, www.skylandtrail.org/survive-a-crisis-situation-with-dbt-distress-tolerance-skills/.

Stern, Manuel, et al. "Blue Light Exposure Decreases Systolic Blood Pressure, Arterial Stiffness and Improves Endothelial Function in Humans." *European Journal of Preventive Cardiology*, vol. 25, no. 17, 10 Sept. 2018, pp. 1875–1883, 10.1177/2047487318800072. Accessed 17 May 2020.

SUDS. *The Distress Thermometer - Subjective Units of Distress Scale (SUDS).*

Suicide and Crisis Lifeline. "Home." *988lifeline.org*, 988lifeline.org.

Sunrisertc. "4 Steps to Happy Relationships." *Sunrise Residential Treatment Center*, 18 Aug. 2017, sunrisertc.com/interpersonal-effectiveness/.

"6 Life Changing Skills to Successfully Manage Your next Emotional Crisis." *Sunrise Reside Treatment Center*, 13 Sept. 2017, sunrisertc.com/distress-tolerance-skills/#soothe. Accessed 18 Nov. 2022.

ttie, Jill. "Does Venting Your Feelings Actually Help?" *Greater Good*, 21 June 2021, greatergood.berkeley.edu/article/item/does_venting_your_feelings_actually_help.

vart, Joan. "3 Easy Mindfulness Exercises to Regulate Your Emotions." *Open Forest*, 20 July 2016, openforest.net/3-easy-mindfulness-exercises/.

herapist Aid. "ABC Model for REBT (Worksheet)." *Therapist Aid*, www.therapistaid.com/therapy-worksheet/abc-model-for-rebt.

nger Iceberg (Worksheet)." *Therapist Aid*, www.therapistaid.com/therapy-worksheet/anger-iceberg/anger/none.

Challenging Negative Thoughts (Worksheet)." *Therapist Aid*, www.therapistaid.com/therapy-worksheet/challenging-negative-thoughts.

gressive Muscle Relaxation Script*. 2014.

erapists Aid. "Introduction to Anger Management (Worksheet)." *Therapist Aid*, www.therapistaid.com/therapy-worksheet/introduction-to-anger-management. Accessed 5 Dec. 2022.

erapy by PRO. "DBT Self Validation Worksheet PDF." *TherapyByPro*, therapybypro.com/product/dbt-self-validation-worksheet/. Accessed 29 Nov. 2022.

erapy by Pro. "DBT Chain Analysis Worksheet PDF." *TherapyByPro*, therapybypro.com/product/dbt-chain-analysis-worksheet-pdf/. Accessed 29 Nov. 2022.

Connor. "Strategies to Redirect Your Thoughts and Distract Your Mind." *Www.uhhospitals.org*, 24 Apr. 2020, www.uhhospitals.org/blog/articles/2020/04/strategies-to-redirect-your-thoughts-and-distract-your-mind. Accessed 25 Nov. 2022.

er, Ken. "Body Scan Meditation - HelpGuide.org." *Https://Www.helpguide.org*, Oct. 2022, www.helpguide.org/meditations/body-scan-meditation.htm.

sters. "Definition of DETRIMENTAL." *Www.merriam-Webster.com*, www.merriam-webster.com/dictionary/detrimental.

s, Katie. "Ice Bath Benefits: How Cold Therapy Improves the Body and the Brain." *Wellness Mama®*, 24 May 2019, wellnessmama.com/health/ice-bath-benefits/. Accessed 17 Nov. 2022.

Mind. "DBT : Wise Mind - Skills, Worksheets, Videos, & Activities." *DBT*, dialecticalbehaviortherapy.com/mindfulness/wise-mind/.

Yates, Brad. "Trust the Process - Tapping with Brad Yates." *Www.youtube.com*, www.youtube.com/watch?v=ZWNq-xkXe4E. Accessed 12 Nov. 2022.

Yuen, Alan W.C., and Josemir W. Sander. "Can Natural Ways to Stimulate the Vagus Nerve Improve Seizure Control?" *Epilepsy & Behavior*, vol. 67, Feb. 2017, pp. 105–110, 10.1016/j.yebeh.2016.10.039. Accessed 23 Mar. 2021.

Zinn, Jon Kabat. "Basic Mindfulness Skills - the Dialectical Behavior Therapy Skills Workbook Practical DBT Exercises for Learning Mindfulness, Interpersonal Effectiveness, Emotion Regulation & ... Tolerance (New Harbinger Self-Help Workbook) 1st Edition." *Doctorlib.info*, 2003, doctorlib.info/psychiatry/dialectical-behavior-therapy/4.html. Accessed 6 Dec. 2022.

Printed in Great Britain
by Amazon

22728429R00176